A PENTECOSTAL APPROACH to BIBLE STUDY

Philippians
A PATH TO JOY

DISCOVERY GUIDE

TABLE OF CONTENTS

FOREWORD

May God's joy and peace be yours! Indeed, these two powerful words, *joy* and *peace*, characterize much of what Paul says in his Epistle to the Philippians. For example, Paul prays for them with joy (1:4). He desires for them to have a joyous faith (1:25). The unity of the Philippians will complete his joy (2:2). They are to receive Epaphroditus with joy (2:29). Finally, Paul goes so far as to say that the Philippians are his joy and crown (4:1).

True spiritual joy is so important in the life of the Christian that Paul commands the Philippians to "rejoice in the Lord" (3:1). He can hardly complete a chapter without twice exhorting them again to rejoice in the Lord (4:4). Paul practices what he preaches, because he rejoices every time the Gospel is proclaimed (1:18). And finally, he rejoices in his service to the Philippians, and they are to join him in this rejoicing (2:17-18).

Why does Paul emphasize the importance of joy in the life of the believer? The Epistle to the Philippians gives us the answer. Paul emphasizes joy because he knows that authentic joy in the Lord is what brings real peace. He knows true peace comes from God (1:2). He knows joyous prayer, full of thanksgiving, invites the peace of God to guard our hearts and minds in Christ Jesus (4:7). For all of these reasons, Paul ends his most encouraging letter in the same way as he began. He prays that "the God of peace" (4:9) surround the Philippians with His special presence.

All of this means that God not only cares about our souls, but that He cares about our minds and hearts as well. God is vitally concerned about what we think and how we feel. Our emotions, attitudes, and thoughts are an imortant part of who we are in Christ. Therefore, all of these important aspects must be discipiled in Christ. So Philippians plays a huge role in our spiritual formation.

Do you want more of God's joy and peace in your life? If so, then this inductive study of Philippians can be your *Path to Joy*. Indeed, you are about to be "drawn into" (the true meaning of *inductive*) a way of worship and service that leads to an ever-increasing joy in the Lord. This is the joy of discipleship! This is the peace that comes from having the mind of Christ Jesus (2:1-5)!

Yet, real spiritual formation does not happen in an instant. That is why discipleship is described as a "walk." As disciples, we are to "walk in the Spirit" (Gal. 5:6). We are to "walk in love" (Eph. 5:2). We are to "walk in light (1 John 1:7). So, true discipleship is a joyous journey of obedience that makes us more like Christ each step of the way (2 John 1:6).

Paul's Epistle to the Philippians provides us with a "pattern" (Rom. 6:17; 2 Tim. 1:13) so that we might "copy" or "mimic" (2 Thess. 3:7, 9; 1 Cor. 4:16; 11:1) the kind of journey that will lead to true joy and peace in the Lord. *Philippians: A Path to Joy* is designed to do just that. This ten-week inductive study of Philippians will guide you along this path, one step at a time. If you are studying on your own, it is suggested that you first work through *A Pentecostal Approach to Bible Study* (obtained from Church of God Adult Discipleship or Pathway Press). This important work will teach you how to study the Bible inductively. Once you have reviewed the basic principles of inductive Bible study (IBS), you will be better prepared to work through this *Discovery Guide* on Philippians. On the other hand, if you are part of a small-group Bible study, the leader of your group can use the first week to teach *A Pentecostal Approach to Bible Study*. Then the whole group will be literally "on the same page" when working through *Philippians: A Path to Joy*. It will be helpful to read Philippians through in one sitting to get a good orientation of the book.

Each lesson of the *Discovery Guide* will cover about half a chapter in Philippians. Thus, the four chapters in the Epistle to the Philippians will consist of eight carefully planned lessons that follow the IBS steps outlined in *A Pentecostal Approach to Bible Study*. Since each lesson is designed to be completed in one week, the study of the text of Philippians will cover eight weeks. Once these lessons have been completed, an additional week will be devoted to summarizing all that you have learned throughout the study; thus making a total of ten weeks.

Each lesson will set forth the steps for doing an inductive study on the assigned lesson. So there is no need to worry about what you need to do to complete a lesson. As you work through Philippians, you will be called upon to develop some creative tools for understanding God's Word. Since no true knowledge of God can be obtained apart from prayer, relevant devotions will accompany each lesson on Philippians. You will also be encouraged to develop your own spiritual journal or log so that you can keep track of your progress as you go deeper into the Scriptures. Finally, you will be challenged to make real change in the Lord, for there can be no discipleship without taking positive steps to be more like Jesus. Yet, most importantly, you will become totally immersed in the Bible and equipped to learn God's Word on your own.

So prepare to receive the joy and peace of the Lord! Let's get started!

William A. Simmons, Ph.D.

A Brief Background

Philippians is one of Paul's most positive and encouraging letters. Indeed, it is often referred to as the "Epistle of Joy" because Paul not only desires his readers to experience the joy of the Lord, he *commands* them to live joy-filled lives in Christ (Phil. 4:4). The entire epistle is filled with the language of rejoicing (1:18; 2:17, 18; 3:1; 4:2, 4) and joy (1:4, 25; 2:2, 29) from beginning to end. The theme of "joy" is made even more remarkable by the fact that Paul has been imprisoned in Rome (1:7, 13, 14, and 17). Moreover, it appears that things have not gone well for him in Rome, for he may be martyred for Christ at any moment (1:20-25; 2:17). Nevertheless, the generosity of the Philippians, the communion of the saints, and the sheer joy of ministry lifts the apostle above the circumstances of this world (1:7; 4:14-18). In this way, Paul serves as the perfect Christian model for the saints of Phillipi. Indeed, they are to "mimmic" the apostle. What a testimony!

So in Philippians, Paul demonstrates the overcoming joy of Christ. He beautifully sets forth the Christian state of mind (2:1-11), and points out the folly of anxiety and worry (4:6). He even gives a prescription for reprogramming the way we think so that we might experience more of the peace of God (4:7, 9).

So in the end, Philippians not only presents us with what it means to be a model Christian, but it also shows us what it means to be a model church. In other words, Philippians is about *discipleship*. It's about making positive change in the Lord. So if you are determined to hold on to negative and dysfunctional ways of thinking, this study is not for you. On the other hand, if you want to be empowered by the joy of the Lord, then read on!

A PENTECOSTAL APPROACH
to
BIBLE STUDY

LESSON ONE

Philippians

1:1-14

THE JOY OF FELLOWSHIP IN CHRIST

Lesson One
Philippians 1:1-14
The Joy of Fellowship in Christ

 ## Key Verse

In all my prayers for all of you, I always pray with joy (Phil. 1:4).

Introduction

You have already made great progress in "inductive Bible study" (IBS)! By reviewing "How to Do an Inductive Bible Study" in *A Pentecostal Approach to Bible Study* (Week One), you have laid a foundation for studying *Philippians: A Path to Joy*. As you study each of the lessons on Philippians, you will apply all of the "Helping Questions" that you learned from *A Pentecostal Approach to Bible Study*. Recall that these are the five W's and one H questions: Who? What? When? Where? Why? and How? You will also devise a number of "Helping Tools" (symbols, underlining, highlighting, etc.) to help you uncover God's truth for yourself. Don't worry about remembering all of the steps and parts of IBS that were set forth in *A Pentecostal Approach to Bible Study*. Each lesson in *Philippians: A Path to Joy* will remind you of what you need to do as you go along. But keep in mind that active, hands-on learning is an essential aspect of any inductive study. By actually *doing* the study and *participating* in group discussions, the truths contained in Philippians will become part of your heart and practice.

So, by the time you finish *Philippians: A Path to Joy*, you will have developed your own study tools to use in any inductive study of the Bible. Also, you will have your own personalized commentary on the Epistle to the Philippians. You are also encouraged to keep a spiritual journal or log of your thoughts and personal commitments to the text of Philippians. This timely record of your work can serve as an invaluable resource in the future. All of this will make your study of Philippians more fun, memorable, and effective.

The format for this study on Philippians will be as follows:

The lesson will begin with a copy of the text to be studied for that week. You will notice that plenty of room has been left between each verse. This space is for you to write in notes, symbols and marks as you work through the lesson. The four-D's of inductive study (**Discover . . . Discern** . . . **Devote . . . Disciple**) will serve as guideposts for your *Path to Joy*. This means your study will always have two major goals in view:

- To learn the content and meaning of Philippians by way of the **Discover** and **Discern** steps.

- To be spiritually transformed through the **Devote** and **Disciple** steps.

It becomes clear that this IBS on Philippians is not just an academic exercise. Rather, it is an important means to spiritual formation. So, as you become discipled by Paul's words in Philippians, and as you disciple others in the wisdom of this great epistle, you are literally fulfilling the Great Commission of Matt. 28:18-20.

Before we get started, we should remind ourselves that there can be no true understanding of God and His Word apart from prayer. This is why each lesson will begin with a section titled, "Pause for Prayer." It is important that we prepare our hearts to receive God's instruction in the Word.

PAUSE *for* PRAYER

After the Jews returned from the Babylonian captivity in about 450 BC, there was a great need to reinstate the Law of God in the land. But when the people heard the awesome power of the Word, they began to weep and mourn, for they had allowed the Bible to fade from memory. That is when Nehemiah exhorted the people to sorrow no more, and said "the joy of the Lord is your strength" (Neh. 8:10). The Scriptures then record, "Then all the people went away to eat and drink, to send portions of food and to celebrate with great joy, because they now understood the words that had been made known to them" (Neh. 8:12).

From this point on, the Jews fortified the city of Jerusalem, reinstated the Law of God in their hearts, and rebuilt the Temple. This means that when we really understand God's Word, it is an occasion for rejoicing. Also, a clear understanding of the Bible gives us strength and hope to accomplish God's will on a number of levels.

Paul also understands that the joy of the Lord brings us strength. This is why, after numerous exhortations to rejoice in Philippians, Paul can say, "I can do all things through Christ which strengtheneth me" (Phil. 4:13 KJV).

 # The Text

Philippians 1:1-14

[1] Paul and Timothy, servants of Christ Jesus, to all God's holy people in Christ Jesus at Philippi, together with the overseers and deacons [2] Grace and peace to you from God our Father and the Lord Jesus Christ. [3] I thank my God every time I remember you. [4] In all my prayers for all of you, I always pray with joy [5] because of your partnership in the gospel from the first day until now, [6] being confident of this, that he who began a good work in you will carry it on to completion until the day of Christ Jesus.

[7] It is right for me to feel this way about all of you, since I have you in my heart and, whether I am in chains or defending and confirming the gospel, all of you share in God's grace with me. [8] God can testify how I long for all of you with the affection of Christ Jesus. [9] And this is my prayer: that your love

may abound more and more in knowledge and depth of insight, ¹⁰ so that you may be able to discern

what is best and may be pure and blameless for the day of Christ, ¹¹ filled with the fruit of righteousness

that comes through Jesus Christ—to the glory and praise of God. ¹² Now I want you to know, brothers

and sisters, that what has happened to me has actually served to advance the gospel. ¹³ As a result, it has

become clear throughout the whole palace guard and to everyone else that I am in chains for Christ.

¹⁴ And because of my chains, most of the brothers and sisters have become confident in the Lord and

dare all the more to proclaim the gospel without fear.

DISCOVER

The apostle John's first word in the Book of Revelation is *apocalupsis,* which literally means

"the unveiling" or "the uncovering" (Rev. 1:1). This is the real purpose of the **Discover** step of IBS.

By way of "Helping Questions" (the five W's and one H questions) you will be able to "*un*-cover" the facts contained in Philippians 1:1-14. The application of "Helping Tools" (underling, highlighting, symbols) is also an important part of the **Discover** step. As you make up your own system to mark special features of the text, the truth of God's Word will begin to shine forth. Indeed, the Greek word for "truth" is *alētheia,* and also means to "*un*-cover." So the **Discover** step is all about using the Helping Questions and Helping Tools to "*dis*-cover" or "*un*-cover" the information contained in the Bible.

The operative word for the **Discover** step is *observation*. You are to *observe* all of the special words and images contained in this passage of scripture. Keen observation begins with a careful reading of Philippians 1:1-14. Don't just skim over this passage. Actively engage the Bible each step of the way. The following Helping Questions will aid you in this active reading of the text.

As you address each one of the Helping Questions, resist the impulse to interpret the Scriptures at this point. This will come a bit later. For now, focus on each question and write out your responses with care. The very act of writing out your answers will help you remember the facts contained in Philippians. The goal is not to get "the right answer." The questions are intended to draw you into the world of the Bible. In fact, the core meaning of *inductive* is "to draw into." So as long as you are "drawn into" the text, you are on target with regard to the Helping Questions.

Sample Helping Questions

Paul identifies himself as an "apostle" in every one of his epistles. It is generally accepted that Paul is defending his apostolic authority by frequently mentioning "apostle" in his letters. Indeed, many churches, such as in Corinth, did not accept that Paul was a true apostle. But this was not the case at Philippi. The church at Philippi was his most trouble-free congregation and they loved the apostle Paul. So it is interesting that in the place where Paul usually puts "apostle" in his epistles, he simply inserts the word *servant*.

- What does this tell you about the relationship between Paul and this special church at Philippi?

ANSWER

Many in the church today question the need for organized church leadership. But in 1:1, Paul addresses the overseers and deacons at Philippi.

- What does this tell you about leadership in the early church and what might this mean for us today? (Note: In responding, it might help to read Acts 14:23; 20:17, 28-30; 1 Tim. 3:1-2; Titus 1:5-7; 1 Peter 5:1-3. Also, some form of the word *deacon* appears in the following verses: Rom. 15:8; 16:1; 1 Cor. 3:15; 2 Cor. 6:4; Gal. 2:17; 1 Tim. 3:8).

ANSWER

_____

_____

_____

_____

_____

_____

_____

_____

_____

_____

_____

_____

_____

Paul is very thankful for the saints at Philippi (read 1:4). He is particularly thankful for the "fellowship" he shares with the Philippians (see 1:5). The word for "fellowship" in Greek is *koinonia* and is the exact same word Paul uses to speak of our "fellowship in the Lord" (read 1 Cor. 1:9) and "fellowship with the Holy Spirit" (see 2 Cor. 13:14).

- How do you think fellowship with one another in the church strengthens our fellowship with the Lord and the Holy Spirit?

ANSWER

Philippians 1:4 has been selected as the key verse for this section. In this verse, Paul mingles together the important concepts of prayer and joy.

- When or under what circumstances have you experienced real joy in prayer?

ANSWER

You will note that Paul's joyous prayer involved a close, personal relationship with the Philippians. This means joy in prayer springs forth from meaningful, interpersonal relationships. That is, *joy* and *koinonia* are interdependent.

Now it is your turn to make up some Helping Questions. This is an important part of IBS. Simply creating and responding to your own questions will "induce" or "draw you into" Paul's words in Philippians. Use the five W's and one H questions to make questions that are important to you. These questions should be framed in a way as to "pry out" facts contained in the text.

So plunge in and craft some questions that will clarify the data contained in this section of scripture.

MY HELPING QUESTIONS AND ANSWERS

MY HELPING QUESTIONS AND ANSWERS CONTINUED

Some additional Helping Questions are listed below. If your list did not include these, respond to them now.

- In 1:7, Paul mentions the "fellowship" or "partnership" he has with the Philippians. "Fellowship" and "partnership" is often rendered "share" in some translations. How have the Philippians shared or helped Paul in the ministry? (In answering this question, you might want to read Phil. 2:25, and 4:10-20.)

ANSWER

- How might the phrase "from the first day until now" in 1:5 relate to Paul's initial meeting with the Philippians in Acts 16:14-15?

ANSWER

- How did Lydia offer "fellowship" in Acts 16:15?

ANSWER

- What does this say about the power of "hospitality" in the church? (Read Rom. 12:13; 1 Peter 4:9; 3 John 1:8.)

ANSWER

- What are some of the terms and expressions of love and affection Paul uses in Phillipians 1:1-14?

ANSWER

- Why do you feel Paul connects "love" in 1:9 with "knowledge," "insight," and the ability "to discern" in 1:9-10? Consider that for the Jews and the early church "knowledge" always involved interpersonal relationships. Could this mean that "knowledge" for the believer is not so much "facts" in our brains as the right spiritual attitude in our hearts? Record your thoughts below.

ANSWER

- How do you think what Paul says in 1:6 applies to his experience as set forth in 1:12-14?

ANSWER

_____

_____

_____

_____

_____

- What do his words here tell us about his belief in "divine sovereignty" or the confidence that "God is in control" (read Rom. 8:28)?

ANSWER

_____

_____

_____

_____

_____

_____

By this point, you have become very familiar with the content of Philippians 1:1-14. This is a good time to review all of your Helping Questions and answers. Summarize your findings by asking yourself, "As a result of my work in verses 1-14, *what facts* have surfaced from the text?" Again, stick to the information you have gleaned from the text and resist the temptation to produce a detailed interpretation at this point. List the data you have obtained from your study.

MY FINDINGS

_____

_____

_____

_____

_____

_____

_____

_____

_____

_____

_____

DISCERN

Now that you have intensely *observed* the content of Philippians 1:1-14 by way of the **Discover** step, you are better prepared to *interpret* its meaning in the **Discern** step of IBS. So, if the **Discover** step is focused on what the Bible *says*, the **Discern** step concentrates on what the Scriptures *mean*.

As outlined in the *A Pentecostal Approach to Bible Study*, this part of IBS invites you to create a number of Helping Tools that will help you understand and learn the Word of God. These Helping Tools consist of a marking system made up of symbols, highlighting, underlining, and so on. So in the **Discern** step you are to clearly identify key words, phrases, and special features of the Bible. These special features might be repetition, parallel ideas, comparison and contrast, and the like. For example, if the word *prayer* is listed several times in your passage, then you might want to insert a symbol of praying hands 🤲. The royal Messiah, Jesus, may be represented as a small crown 👑. The blood of Jesus might be underlined in red and references to geographic locations could be marked in brown.

You can see how the **Discern** step of IBS can be an enjoyable part of Bible study. But there is a serious aspect here as well. The marking system you create must make sense to you, *and* you need to be consistent in its use. That is, if red means the blood of Christ in the first lesson, then *red* should mean the blood of Christ in the last lesson. In this way, you will be able to track a particular theme from the first verse until the last.

Herein lies the real purpose of the Helping Tools—to help you see what was really important to the writers of Scripture. If Paul repeats "joy" in Philippians, then "joy" is a central theme of the epistle. If "joy" is consistently joined to "prayer," then the message is clear: there can be no true joy of the Lord apart from prayer. This means the Helping Tools of the **Discern** step get you into the mind of the author. For example, if Paul opens a section with an emphasis on the Holy Spirit and then ends that section in the same way, then everything he has said has been literally wrapped in the Holy Spirit. Good Helping Tools will bring these important features to light.

If you stick with the creative development of Helping Tools, in time the process will become second nature to you. You will no longer be content with simply reading the Scriptures. Rather, you will actively study the Bible to *discover* want it says, *discern* what it means, and seek genuine change through the Word (in other words, to be discipled in the Lord).

None of this can happen apart from the Spirit of God. Indeed, "discerning of spirits" is one of the spiritual gifts listed in 1 Corinthians 12:10. The Greek word used for "discerning" here is *diakriseis* and means "to make an informed distinction; to differentiate." The Helping Questions you have developed as well as the Helping Tools you have created will aid you in making an "informed distinction" with regard to God's Word.

Recall that the **Discern** step is about *interpretation* and this, too, is an important aspect of the gifts of the Holy Spirit. In 1 Corinthians 12:10. Paul speaks about the gift of interpretation. Here

Paul uses the word *hermeneia* from which we get the word *hermeneutics*, in other words, "the art of interpretation." The core meaning of the word *hermeneia* is "to unseal." Also, it is interesting to note that Paul speaks of interpretation in 1 Corinthians 12:30; 14:13, 27. Here he uses a stronger form of the word, meaning "to *thoroughly* unseal."

The Holy Spirit can help you "thoroughly unseal" the meaning of Philippians by way of your Helping Questions and Helping Tools. Yet as your study has already revealed, sincere, faith-filled prayer is required to receive anything from the Lord (James 1:6).

PAUSE *for* PRAYER

As you commence this **Discern** portion of your study, you should know that your journey into God's Word is really a journey into the very heart of God. Paul makes the same point when he says,

> *Which things also we speak, not in the words which man's wisdom teacheth, but which the Holy Ghost teacheth; comparing spiritual things with spiritual. But the natural man receiveth not the things of the Spirit of God: for they are foolishness unto him: neither can he know them, because they are spiritually discerned* (1 Cor. 2:13-14 KJV).

As you pray for God's guidance in interpreting the Bible, keep in mind that it is the Holy Spirit that teaches us about the heart of God. Know, too, that it is the Holy Spirit that enables us to discern the things of God. Pray now that the Holy Spirit will teach you and grant the kind of discernment that will empower you to fully interpret His Word.

Reread Philippians 1:1-14 *completely through once again*, but this time call to remembrance some of the truths that have emerged as a result of the Helping Questions. Have your colored pencils and markers close at hand so you can create your own system for highlighting important aspects of this passage. Here are some tips that can guide you in developing your marking system (your Helping Tools).

- Paul is very positive in this passage. You might want to mark each positive word with a + sign. Some suggested words to mark are: *thank, joy, fellowship, confident, love, excellence, boldness.*

- The phrase "until the day of Christ Jesus" (1:6) points to the second coming of Jesus (see also 3:20). Much more "end time" language will be used in Philippians (see also 1:10). Mark elements that indicate the end time.

- As noted, the word for "fellowship" is *koinōnia* and is very similar to the word for "share" or "partnership" (1:7). Make a symbol for *fellowship, sharing,* or *partnership.* There will be many more instances of these kinds of words in Philippians.

- "Defending" in 1:7 is a legal term that refers to the kind of defense given in a court of law. Also "confirming" (verse 7 again) refers to the kind of evidence in court that supports a case. Paul is facing a final trial before Caesar in Rome, and much "law court" language will be used in Philippians. Develop a symbol or mark for legal language and imagery. You will find it useful in the lessons to come.

- The word for "advance" in 1:12 is a military term that describes making progress or forging ahead through hostile territory. Philippi had a proud military tradition and Paul taps into this imagery to connect with the Philippians. Create a way to highlight ideas like *soldier, guard, protect,* etc., because Paul uses such words throughout Philippians.

- A case in point concerning military jargon is found in 1:13. The word for "palace" in verse13 is the Latin term *praitōri* and could be translated "palace guard." This refers to the "Praetorian

Guard" of the emperor at the time, Nero Caesar. The Praetorian Guard numbered about 6,000 elite soldiers who were committed to protecting the emperor. So Paul really is preaching the gospel in Rome! (Read Acts 23:11; Rom. 1:15.)

There is so much more in this passage! Take time to mark everything you feel is significant. You will find that throughout Philippians, Paul is going to return to the themes and ideas he sets forth in verses 1-14. If you do a good job here, it will pay big dividends throughout your entire study.

➡PULLING IT ALL TOGETHER⬅

Now is the time to draw upon all that you have learned through the use of your Helping Tools. That is, all of the your hard work has "*un*-covered" (recall the meaning of *apokalupsis*?) many important facts and features contained in Philippians 1:1-14. Carefully trace out the significance of your Helping Tools and "pull together" or integrate what you have learned thus far.

The following questions will serve as a framework for summarizing your findings here.

- Examine your marking system. Do you see any repetitions of words or ideas? Such repetitions indicate these are important ideas for Paul and the Philippians. Write down what you have discovered in the space provided.

ANSWER

ANSWER CONTINUED

_____
_____
_____
_____
_____
_____
_____
_____
_____

- Have you highlighted any features that relate to "mind" or "thinking" in 1:1-14? The "Christian state of mind" is an important theme in Philippians, so you will want to make sure to accent items that relate here.

ANSWER

_____
_____
_____
_____
_____
_____
_____
_____

- • One of the themes of this section is that "God is in Control!" (See 1:6.) How might this relate to 1:12-13? Compare what Paul says here with Acts 23:11 and Rom. 1:15.

ANSWER

Now that you have gleaned all of the special features that have emerged from your Helping Tools, you are in a much better position to interpret Philippians 1:1-14. Moreover, if you gather up all of the truth (remember the meaning of the Greek word *alētheia*?) you discovered by way of your Helping Questions, you are now able to "unseal" (*hermeneia* again!) the meaning of this important passage of Scripture.

In the space provided below, use what you have learned thus far to answer the question, "What is God saying in this passage?" But don't stop there. When writing out your interpretation, be sure to include some thoughts on, "What is God saying *to me* through this passage?"

MY INTERPRETATION

DEVOTE

The operative word for the **Discover** step was *observation*. The main idea in the **Discern** step was *interpretation*. But now the important concepts in the **Devote** step are *commitment* and *obedience*. Since you understand what the text *says* and also what the text *means*, you are now ready to be truly "drawn into" (Do you still recall the meaning of "inductive"?) the spiritual mandates of the Bible. That is, you are now to commit to the spiritual and moral claims found in Philippians 1:1-14. It is here that you may sincerely ask yourself the question, "In light of what I now know about the Scriptures, what does the Lord want me to do?" In other words, it is time to ask the Holy Spirit to apply the lessons of Philippians 1:1-14 to your heart.

It is clear that the **Devote** step is the most personal part of the whole study. This aspect of IBS must surely be surrounded in prayer.

PAUSE *for* PRAYER

Throughout Philippians, Paul is concerned about the Christian state of mind. That is, God is not just interested in saving our souls; He is interested in the health of our minds and emotions as well. In the same vein, in 2 Corinthians 10:4-5 Paul states,

For the weapons of our warfare are not carnal, but mighty through God to the pulling down of strong holds; casting down imaginations, and every high thing that exalteth itself against the knowledge of God, and bringing into captivity every thought to the obedience of Christ (KJV).

Jesus does not only want to be Lord of our soul, but He wants to be Lord over our heart and our attitudes as well. Paul's concern for our "inner world" can be seen in his frequent use of commands in Philippians. That is, a Godly state of mind is not simply an option for the believer; it is a divine requirement. So the question we are to ask ourselves at this point in the study is, "Are there areas of my heart that need to come under the authority of God's Word in Philippians 1:1-14?" Or, "Do I harbor certain attitudes that conflict with what God has said in this section of Scripture?"

The following are some questions that may help you to *devote* yourself to the kind of encouragement and change set forth in Philippians 1:1-14. This would be a good time to work in your journal or spiritual log. Jot down a few descriptions of your internal world that you feel the Lord can help you with. Survey the landscape of your heart, so to speak, and write out the kinds of help that would make you a stronger, better person.

Just within Philippians 1:3-4, Paul speaks of the following qualities:

- Thankfulness (v. 3)
- Prayerfulness (v. 4)
- Joy (v. 4)
- Fellowship (v. 5)
- Confidence (v. 6)

As you *devote* yourself to the claims of this text, take stock of your thoughts and attitudes.

- On a scale of 1-10, how thankful are you in your spirit? Do you generally come across to others as a thankful person?

- The Scriptures exhort us to "pray without ceasing" (1 Thess. 5:17 KJV). This must mean that we are to be in continual communion with the Lord in prayer. That is, for the believer there are not just specific times to pray, but rather a general attitude of prayer is to characterize those in Christ. To what extent is your mind taken up with a continual attitude of prayer? Could you devote more of your thought world to intercessory prayer rather than "wasting thoughts" on prayerless chatter?

- After studying Philippians 1:1-14, do you feel that the Lord would have you experience more joy in your life?

- Paul was a strong and accomplished person (Phil. 3:4-6), but he knew that ministering for the Lord is a team effort. That is why he is so thankful for those who helped him in ministry.

- Are you one who welcomes partnerships, or are you a "lone ranger"? To what extent are you willing to accept the help of others *and* to request the help of others?

- Paul's confidence is in the Lord, not in himself. How do you feel that such confidence in the Lord would affect your emotional and mental attitude?

☧ DISCIPLE

A major purpose for studying the Bible is to undergo positive change in the Lord. Indeed, this is the true meaning of discipleship. As the Spirit actualizes the will of God in our lives, we become more like the image of Christ (Rom. 8:29). Moreover, as we come under the discipline of the Word, we are better equipped to disciple others in the Lord.

The **Disciple** step of IBS is a call to *action*. This means that the critical question of the **Disciple** step is, "What does the Scripture *require me to do*?" This is where you can make real plans to actualize what you have learned in Philippians. The following comments may help you "incarnate" or make the Bible real in your life.

This week, in light of what I have learned from Philippians 1:1-14, I commit to . . .

- Expressing thanks to God and others for a minimum of ten times a day. (Keep a record!)

- Pray without ceasing. That is, I will intentionally monitor the internal dialogue of my mind and heart and devote as much as possible to prayer.

- Stop depending on the things of this world to bring me joy. Regardless of my situation in life, I pledge to take hold of the joy of the Lord!

- Seek God's help in trusting in Him more. I refuse to worry. Rather, I will set aside all anxious thoughts and replace them with a joyous confidence in God.

- Becoming more of a team player rather than trying to do everything by myself. I will accept that life in Christ is a matter of community and not a "solo flight" through this world.

The Great Commission (Matt. 28:8-20) commanded that we are not only to be taught in the Word, but we are to go out and teach others (disciple them) through the Word. There are so many people who really need the joy of the Lord, and Philippians can help them. Perhaps more to the point, *you* can help them in your newfound understanding of Philippians. So be on the lookout for those who might be in desperate need of the joy of the Lord. Also, help another person experience the liberating truth that they don't have to do everything by themselves. There are members in the body of Christ who have the spiritual gift of "helps," and they need a place to minister (see 1 Cor. 12:28)! Finally, teach someone about the empowering presence of prayer. Let them know there is always something they can do about their situation in life; they can pray!

A PENTECOSTAL APPROACH *to* BIBLE STUDY

LESSON TWO

Philippians

1:15-30

THE JOY OF SUFFERING
FOR THE GOSPEL

Lesson Two
Philippians 1:15-30
The Joy of Suffering for the Gospel

 KEY VERSE

For to you it has been granted on behalf of Christ, not only to believe in Him, but also to suffer for His sake (Phil. 1:29 NKJV).

Introduction

By carefully working through lesson one, you have accomplished two major goals. First, you have learned the basic principles of IBS and put these principles into practice. Second, you have already placed your hand on the pulse of the apostle Paul in Philippians. These two accomplishments will serve you well as you continue to dig into this wonderful Word from the Lord.

Paul is an excellent writer and, in all of his epistles, he incorporates the literary quality of "cohesion." That is, all parts of his letter "connect together." So what you have learned in lesson one will be reflected in what Paul says in lesson two, and so on to the end of the epistle. This is one of the reasons why you should really focus on your Helping Questions and Helping Tools. One thing builds upon another until you have a very sure grasp on the Bible.

In Philippians 1:15-30, Paul continues to deal with matters of the heart. His words are so rich that the real power of what he says can easily escape us if we only give a "quick read" of the Word. The **Discover** step of IBS is designed to slow us down so we can be "drawn into" (the core meaning of "inductive") his letter to the Philippians. Yet when we do take the time to examine the Bible closely, there is so much there that it can be overwhelming! That is why this IBS breaks the study down into four parts: **Discover** . . . **Discern** . . . **Devote** . . . **Disciple**. Each part takes on an important aspect of study and application and presents this one step after another.

PAUSE *for* PRAYER

So let's enter into the first step of IBS, the **Discover** step, and begin our *Path to Joy*.

Only Spirit can reveal Spirit. As Paul shares with the Corinthians:

> *But God hath revealed them unto us by his Spirit: for the Spirit searcheth all things, yea, the deep things of God. For what man knoweth the things of a man, save the spirit of man which is in him? even so the things of God knoweth no man, but the Spirit of God* (1 Cor. 2:10-11 KJV).

In other words, we cannot "manhandle" the Bible. We can apply all of the study techniques we want, but unless the Spirit reveals and applies God's Word to our hearts (like the scribes and the Pharisees) our study is in vain. Pray now that the Holy Spirit will help you to *dis*-cover the true meaning of Paul's letter to the Philippians so that you might truly understand and apply it to your heart.

 # THE TEXT

Philippians 1:15-30 (NKJV)

15Some indeed preach Christ even from envy and strife, and some also from goodwill: 16 The former preach Christ from selfish ambition, not sincerely, supposing to add affliction to my chains; 17 but the latter out of love, knowing that I am appointed for the defense of the gospel. 18 What then? Only that in every way, whether in pretense or in truth, Christ is preached; and in this I rejoice, yes, and will rejoice.

19 For I know that this will turn out for my deliverance through your prayer and the supply of the Spirit of Jesus Christ, 20 according to my earnest expectation and hope that in nothing I shall be ashamed,

but with all boldness, as always, so now also Christ will be magnified in my body, whether by life or by death. [21] For to me, to live is Christ, and to die is gain. [22] But if I live on in the flesh, this will mean fruit from my labor; yet what I shall choose I cannot tell. [23] For I am hard-pressed between the two, having a desire to depart and be with Christ, which is far better. [24] Nevertheless to remain in the flesh is more needful for you. [25] And being confident of this, I know that I shall remain and continue with you all for your progress and joy of faith, [26] that your rejoicing for me may be more abundant in Jesus Christ by my coming to you again. [27] Only let your conduct be worthy of the gospel of Christ, so that whether I come and see you or am absent, I may hear of your affairs, that you stand fast in one spirit, with one mind striving together for the faith of the gospel, [28] and not in any way terrified by your adversaries, which is to them a proof of perdition, but to you of salvation, and that from God. [29] For to you it has been granted on behalf of Christ, not only to believe in Him, but also to suffer for His sake, [30] having

the same conflict which you saw in me and now hear is in me.

DISCOVER

Note again that plenty of room has been left between the verses for you to mark, highlight, and insert symbols in the **Discern** step of IBS. But for now, you are to busy yourself with *un*-covering the facts contained in Philippians 1:15-30. Do not worry about what the Bible means at this stage, but really focus on what the Bible says, for right now. Everything you will be doing here will enhance your ability to give a good interpretation later.

First, carefully read through Philippians 1:15-30. Don't just skim over the text, but intensely observe what it says. This is the main task of the **Discover** part of IBS. Really scour every line to extract all of the facts contained in this portion of the Bible.

Once you feel you have a good "lay of the land," so to speak, it's time to "dig into" the text. The following Helping Questions (the Who? What? When? Where? Why? and How? questions) will help you do just that.

Sample Helping Questions

- Where is Paul physically at the time of this writing? (You may want to look back over your work in lesson one for this answer. Read also Phil. 1:17).

ANSWER

- Who would preach the gospel insincerely to add to Paul's suffering (1:15-18)?

ANSWER

- Why do you think anyone would want to do that to Paul?

ANSWER

- How can Paul say that Christ will be exalted, regardless of whether he is released from prison or whether he is executed (1:19-20)?

ANSWER

- What does 1:21 say about Paul's confidence in the sovereign direction of God over his life?

ANSWER

These sample questions should give you an idea of how to develop your own **Discover** questions. So take a few moments to creatively pose some relevant questions to Philippians 1:15-30. The very process of thinking about these questions helps you to focus more intently on what Paul says at this point. Of course, your question anticipates the answer, and this is also a good thing. So work with the Who? What? When? Where? Why? and How? questions to really pry out the content of this passage. Record your work in the space provided.

MY HELPING QUESTIONS AND ANSWERS

MY HELPING QUESTIONS AND ANSWERS CONTINUED

Here are a few more examples that may help to garner a few more facts from Philippians 1:15-30.

- What kind of uncertainty can you detect in Paul's heart in 1:20-24?

ANSWER

- How can Paul express uncertainty and confidence at the same time? (See 1:19, 25, 27.) Is he working on two levels here, that is, on the level of mere human feelings and perception, and then addressing his future within the context of faith in God?

ANSWER

• What kind of value does Paul assign to suffering in the life of the Christian (1:28-30)?

ANSWER

By way of your Helping Questions, you have already gathered a considerable amount of facts on Philippians 1:15-30. It would be good to go over your findings at this time and summarize them below.

MY FINDINGS

MY FINDINGS CONTINUED

_____

_____

_____

_____

_____

_____

_____

_____

_____

_____

_____

 # DISCERN

Now that you have a good grasp on what the text says, you can feel more confident in arriving at what the text means. The **Discern** part of IBS is where, with the help of the Spirit, you *un*-seal (recall the root meaning of *hermeneutics*?) the core message of this passage. But before we do, let's prepare our hearts for God to speak to us through His Word.

PAUSE *for* PRAYER

"Though he were a Son, yet learned he obedience by the things which he suffered" (Heb. 5:8 KJV). What a statement! The very Son of God learned to submit to God's will by the things He suffered. How much more then, do we need to have our spiritual eyes wide open when we are in the midst of suffering. It could be that we seek release from hard times too soon! God may be doing His best Kingdom work in our lives when we are going through hard times. Pray now that we not only learn from God in the prosperous times in our lives, but that we be open to learn from God during the lean times as well.

Just as you did in lesson one, the **Discern** step of IBS uses Helping Tools to color-code, underline, and symbolize significant aspects of the Bible. These items might include key words, repetitions, comparison and contrast, geographic location, time references, and the like. Remember that you are in the process of developing your own "tool box" of Helping Tools for studying the Bible. So be creative, but also be consistent in your use of Helping Tools. If a "↑" sign stood for a positive emotion in lesson one, then stick with this symbol for the rest of your study in Philippians. In this way, by the time you finish, you can rapidly skim over the whole book and draw out all of the passages that deal with positive emotions by quickly noting all of the "↑" signs in the text.

Here are some areas of Philippians 1:15-30 that might warrant your attention in employing your Helping Tools:

- Paul continues to contrast both positive and negative emotions and motives in this section. You may want to continue to use some symbol or marking to note the "up" factors in 1:15-30 and contrast these with the "down" factors as well.

- Some of these contrasting factors consist of "sincerity" and "insincerity" (1:15-18).

- The word for "affliction" in 1:16 is *thlipsis*. It is from this word that we get the English word *friction*. There are some insincere preachers of the gospel who want to add "friction" to the rubbing and chaffing of Paul's bonds. Develop some markings for pain and suffering for your study of 1:15-30.

- Paul expresses both confidence and doubt in this section (1:19-26). Overall he is positive about his future, but there is some uncertainty in his words as well. You may want to develop some symbol like "~" to convey Paul's lack of clarity about what lies ahead for him.

These pointers should help you build upon the marking system you have already developed for Philippians 1:1-14. In this way you will expand the number and kinds of markings, color-coding, and symbols. Soon you will have a way of noting almost every major theme and item in the Bible. When you become comfortable with your own way of highlighting important aspects of the Word, you will no longer be content with just skimming over the lines on a page of scripture. As you no doubt have experienced many times, a surface reading of the Bible does not stay with you long and has little impact on you or on those you come in contact with. But, if you actively wrestle with the Word and develop a system for tagging important and repeated themes, these truths will go deep into your heart and stay there. Then they can more easily be retrieved and used in your own discipleship and the discipleship of others the Lord leads you to.

So with marking tools in hand, creatively work through Philippians 1:15-30, reusing items that helped in lesson one, yet developing some new ways to discern the Scriptures in this section.

➡**PULLING IT ALL TOGETHER**⬅

Now that you have developed and answered a number of Helping Questions and accented important parts with your Helping Tools, it's time to "pull it all together." Here you will make a summary of everything you have learned about Philippians 1:15-30. So reread all of your Helping Questions and your answers. Take some time to get the "big picture" that has emerged as a result of your Helping Tools.

Once you are confident that you have a grasp on the fruit of your work, summarize your findings below.

MY FINDINGS

MY FINDINGS CONTINUED

Here are a few more tips that may help you in this regard:

- Paul addresses two kinds of individuals in 1:15-30—those who want to help him and those who want to hurt him.

- Paul wrestles with two competing aspects of his heart: (1) hope that he will soon be released so he can visit and minister among the Philippians, and (2) the real possibility that he will soon be executed.

Now, with all of this in hand, write out your interpretation.

MY INTERPRETATION

MY INTERPRETATION CONTINUED

_____
_____
_____
_____
_____
_____
_____
_____

DEVOTE

In some ways, Paul's words in this section are hard to understand. He expresses gratitude for the Philippians but is disheartened by the insincerity he finds in the church. He expresses hope for a positive outcome at his trial, but he is realistic enough to know that he might be executed. Nevertheless, the overriding factor in all of this is his faith in God. Regardless of what happens to him, Paul is in the palm of God's loving and protecting hands. So in the mix of the good and the bad, the hopeful and the discouraging, Paul can rejoice that the Kingdom will prevail and the Gospel will continue to advance. In like manner, let's devote ourselves to the high calling placed before us in Philippians 1:15-30.

PAUSE *for* PRAYER

In the midst of the Babylonian captivity of the Jews, the prophet Jeremiah asks the Lord, "Wherefore doth the way of the wicked prosper? Wherefore are all they happy that deal very treacherously?" (Jer. 12:1 KJV). Paul must have asked this question too: *Why are insincere preachers enjoying freedom and I am confined in prison?* Yet, both great men of God were able to rise above the level of mere mortality and see the plan of God. They came to realize that, through suffering, God was working out a higher and more lasting good in their lives than if everything was pleasant and enjoyable. Let's pray that God will grant us the spiritual maturity and vision to devote ourselves to the vision that He has for us and not be confined to the dim view the world would have us see.

☩⋉ DISCIPLE

As you have already gathered, an inductive approach to the Bible is not content with us just having good thoughts about God. Rather, IBS promises something more. A primary goal of IBS is that we undergo positive change in the Lord in light of what we have learned from the Scriptures. With this in mind, we should take concrete steps to make God's Word become more real in our lives. Prayerfully consider the challenges listed below and ask God to help you be discipled in this manner.

This week, I commit to . . .

- Not allowing the shortcomings of others to steal my joy in the Lord

- Trusting that God is in control of my life and that as I submit to Him in love, He will direct my paths (Prov. 3:5)

- Embracing suffering as an effective work of the Lord in my life—a work that can accomplish more in a short time than "smooth sailing" can get done in a lifetime.

These spiritual mandates are designed to take us to a higher level of discipleship. Perhaps you know of some believers who are in need of a "growth spurt" at this point in their lives. They are too easily distracted by ill-motivated "believers." They allow their joy to be stolen from them by the slightest setbacks and frustrations. It may be that, as a result of your own commitment to Philippians 1:15-30, God can use you to disciple them along Paul's *Path to Joy.*

LESSON THREE

Philippians

2:1-18

THE JOY OF HAVING
THE MIND OF CHRIST

LESSON THREE
Philippians 2:1-18
The Joy of Having the Mind of Christ

KEY VERSE

In your relationships with one another, have the same mindset as Christ Jesus (Phil. 2:5).

Introduction

You have come a long way in your study of Philippians. By using the four "D's" of inductive study (**Discover** . . . **Discern** . . . **Devote** . . . **Disciple**), you have already analyzed the text for facts, highlighted the Scriptures for patterns and emphases, interpreted its meaning, personally committed yourself to the voice of God in the Bible, and made plans to actualize this Word in your life and the lives of others. Whew! All of this, and you have just completed the first chapter! And there is so much more to the extraordinarily positive message of Philippians.

The following is a brief review of some of the truths you have learned from the first chapter:

- Paul clearly feels very comfortable in his relationship with the Philippians. He is not defensive about his apostolic authority, and he expresses real joy for their faith and service in the Lord.

3

- Paul refuses to allow his present circumstances to control his heart, mind, and spirit. In spite of his imprisonment, Paul is filled with the joy of the Lord!

- Paul has absolute confidence that God is in control. God will complete the good work he has begun in the Philippians. God will even use ill-motivated preachers to advance the Gospel. Even if Paul is martyred for the faith, God will use that too to build the Kingdom.

Yet, most importantly, you have committed yourself to the spiritual challenges of Philippians. This means that you have been discipled in the Word. Also, if you have been able to share what you have learned with others, then you have obeyed the Great Commission of our Lord in Matthew 28:19-20.

As you reflect on your study of chapter one, and prepare to be immersed in chapter two, continue to pray for the guidance of the Holy Spirit. Pray that He draws you into (induct!) the life-changing message of Philippians. For as you allow your mind, heart, and spirit to be completely directed by the Word, you will be drawn nearer to the very heart of God (James 4:8).

PAUSE *for* PRAYER

Much of what Paul says in Philippians 2:1-18 has to do with proper Christian attitudes. In this section, he clearly affirms the virtue of Christian humility. He points to Christ as our prime example of One who humbly submits to the will of God (2:5-11). In this sense, Paul, James and Peter stand shoulder to shoulder in affirming that "God resists the proud, but gives grace to the humble" (1 Peter

5:5 NKVJ). Pray now that God will grant you the spirit of humility so that, as in the case of Christ, God can exalt you in due season.

 # THE TEXT

Philippians 2:1-18

[1] Therefore if you have any encouragement from being united with Christ, if any comfort from his love, if any common sharing in the Spirit, if any tenderness and compassion, [2] then make my joy complete by being like-minded, having the same love, being one in spirit and of one mind. [3] Do nothing out of selfish ambition or vain conceit. Rather, in humility value others above yourselves, [4] not looking to your own interests but each of you to the interests of the others. [5] In your relationships with one another, have the same mindset as Christ Jesus: [6] Who, being in very nature God, did not consider equality with God something to be used to his own advantage; [7] rather, he made himself nothing by taking the

very nature of a servant, being made in human likeness. [8] And being found in appearance as a man, he

humbled himself by becoming obedient to death—even death on a cross! [9] Therefore God exalted

him to the highest place and gave him the name that is above every name, [10] that at the name of Jesus

every knee should bow, in heaven and on earth and under the earth, [11] and every tongue acknowledge

that Jesus Christ is Lord, to the glory of God the Father. [12] Therefore, my dear friends, as you have

always obeyed—not only in my presence, but now much more in my absence—continue to work out

your salvation with fear and trembling, [13] for it is God who works in you to will and to act in order to

fulfill his good purpose. [14] Do everything without grumbling or arguing, [15] so that you may become

blameless and pure, "children of God without fault in a warped and crooked generation." Then you will

shine among them like stars in the sky [16] as you hold firmly to the word of life. And then I will be able to boast on the day of Christ that I did not run or labor in vain. ¹⁷ But even if I am being poured out

like a drink offering on the sacrifice and service coming from your faith, I am glad and rejoice with all

of you. ¹⁸ So you too should be glad and rejoice with me.

DISCOVER

The **Discover** step is all about sifting out the facts contained in the Bible. So you will want to

key in on your sense of observation in this phase of the study. First, carefully read Philippians 2:1-18.

Now that you have some experience with the IBS method, you know that, as you read, you should be

on the lookout for ideas and words that are essential to this passage. Your concern here is with the facts

that make up the content of this portion of the Bible. Again, hold off on making interpretations at this

point. Rather, use all of your powers of observation to glean every bit of important material from this

passage.

Now that you have become thoroughly familiar with how the text reads, you can increase your

knowledge of the text by applying your Helping Questions. Recall that these are the Who? What?

When? Where? Why? and How? questions that will help you to *dis*-cover the facts in this beautiful

passage of scripture.

The following are some sample Helping Questions to get you started on this inspiring, yet challenging, part of the Bible.

Sample Helping Questions

Comfort, peace, joy . . . these are some of the words that characterize Paul's letter to the Philippians.

- What are some of the "comfort" words Paul uses in 2:1? List them in the space provided.

ANSWER
_____
_____
_____
_____

- What are some of the "unity" words Paul uses in 2:2? List these words below.

ANSWER
_____
_____
_____
_____

- Why do you feel Paul mentions "selfish ambition" and "vain conceit" in 2:2?

ANSWER

Although Paul is very affirming of the Philippians, he clearly knows something about the "atmosphere" in the church at Philippi (as evidenced in 2:2 and 4:2).

- How do you think Paul may have heard about the interpersonal "climate" that existed in the church at Philippi? (In answering this question, you may want to read Phil. 2:25-30.)

ANSWER

Paul was not one of the original twelve apostles of the Lord. In fact, as "Saul of Tarsus" (Acts 9:11; 11:25), he severely persecuted the church (1 Cor. 15:9; Gal. 1:13, 22ff.; Phil. 3:6; 1 Tim. 1:13). Yet, Phil. 2:5-11 clearly indicates that Paul knows something about the life of Jesus of Nazareth.

- What does Paul know about Jesus from these verses?

ANSWER

Philippians 2:1-18 contains some of the most theologically important statements in the New Testament. Many more Helping Questions are needed to draw out the information contained in these verses. Take some time to make up your own Helping Questions. Remember that your Helping Questions should be designed to draw out the important data contained in this section. Write out your Helping Questions and answers below.

MY HELPING QUESTIONS AND ANSWERS

_____

_____

_____

_____

_____

_____

_____

_____

_____

_____

_____

_____

_____

_____

The following are a few more Helping Questions. If you have not included these in your list, respond to them now.

Philippians 2:5-11 is often referred to as the "Kenosis Passage." *Kenosis* is a Greek word that can be translated "empty" or "humble."

- How do you think Paul is describing Christ in 2:8? Did Jesus "humble" Himself in the Incarnation or does Paul mean that Jesus "emptied" Himself when He became a human?

ANSWER

For mere mortals like us, "death" is not a matter of "obedience"; we just naturally die. But Paul says that Jesus was "obedient unto death" (2:8).

- Why would Paul describe death for Jesus as a matter of obedience?

ANSWER

Now that you have carefully read this passage (hopefully more than once!), you have noticed that Philippians 2:5-11 describes a kind of theological movement. That is, if you note where Jesus is at the beginning of the passage (2:6), then trace where He is in the middle of this passage (2:7-8) and next follow the path of Jesus to His final place at the end of the passage (2:9-11), there is a "shape" to the route Jesus took in saving us.

- How would one draw the path Jesus took to save us as set forth in 2:5-11? (Draw a little diagram below reflecting the "theological movement" of Jesus in this passage).

ANSWER

In 2:12, Paul commands the Philippians to "work out [their] own salvation" but in 2:13 he says "for it is God who works in you." These statements seem to contradict one another.

- Who is "working out" our salvation—us or God? Or in some way, could it be both? Note your thoughts.

ANSWER

_____

_____

_____

_____

_____

_____

Paul's words in 2:1-18 are jam-packed with information! Your dialogue with the Helping Questions has uncovered many important points contained in this important part of the Bible. It would be good to take a few moments and review all that you have "dug up" thus far. Summarize your findings in the space provided below.

MY FINDINGS

_____

_____

_____

_____

MY FINDINGS CONTINUED

_____

_____

_____

_____

_____

_____

_____

DISCERN

You now have a fairly good grasp of the content of Philippians 2:1-18. You are moving closer to the point of forming your own interpretation of what this passage means. The **Discern** step will provide even more data upon which to base your interpretation of Philippians. It is here that you will once again access your Helping Tools and mark special words, phrases, and features contained in this passage.

If some of the symbols and markings you have already used in chapter one apply to your studies in chapter two, then by all means use them again. In this way, you will become consistent in your use of the Helping Tools. The consistent use of a personalized marking system is important. It can become a good "habit" for studying the Bible. From now on, you will not simply skim over the Word. With the help of the Holy Spirit and prayer, you will actively engage the Scriptures by gathering together all of the facts and features of a text and then move on to a more informed interpretation of the Bible.

As you have already realized, Paul's letter to the Philippians is packed with prayer. As you prepare to apply your Helping Tools, read the following devotional thought and pray that the Spirit will guide you in the understanding of this powerful Word from the Lord.

PAUSE *for* PRAYER

In 2:1-18, Paul is very concerned about the "inner world" of the Christian. Also, as you will soon discover, his words sound like a hymn or psalm, especially in 2:5-11. It is interesting to note that the psalmist was also concerned about the "inner world" of the believer. In Psalm 51:12, David prays, "Restore to me the joy of your salvation and grant me a willing spirit, to sustain me." In this psalm, David joins together "joy" and "a willing spirit" (that is, "obedience"). Paul does the same in Philippians 2:2 and 12. Can you pray now that God grant you that powerful combination of joy and obedience as you prepare to use your Helping Tools?

When applying Helping Tools to 2:1-18, you may want to highlight the following aspects of this passage:

- Recall the marks and symbols you have already used to highlight emotional aspects of the text in chapter one. You will need these because Paul continues to focus on important emotions and feelings in 2:1-18. Some are positive traits such as "encouragement," "comfort," "fellowship," "tenderness," and "compassion." All of these qualities are included in the very first verse (2:1)! But there are a lot more examples of inner attitudes in this passage. Some of these are quite negative, like "selfish ambition" and "vain conceit" in 2:3. So search these out and mark them in the text.

- Philippians contains a very high "Christology" or "study of Christ." Paul clearly wants to point out the genuine humanity of Jesus, but he also wants to affirm His true divinity. You may want to make a symbol that denotes the humanity of Jesus and then another one that speaks to the divinity of Jesus.

- Another feature of Philippians is that we are personally responsible for doing the right thing (2:12). On the other hand, Paul also emphasizes that God is in complete control (2:13). It might help if you made up one marking system that denotes our responsibility before the Lord, and another one that addresses God's sovereign guidance of our lives. These features will be repeated throughout Philippians.

These suggestions should be enough to set you on the right track for using your Helping Tools in 2:1-18. So review what you have done in the first chapter and look for similar features in chapter two. But be prepared to make up some *new* marking features. There is a good possibility that they will apply to subsequent portions of Philippians.

➡PULLING IT ALL TOGETHER⬅

By this point, you have really scoured 2:1-18. You have gained a thorough knowledge of its content by way of the Helping Questions. You also have a handle on all of its special features through the use of your Helping Tools. The goal now is to integrate everything you have learned and observed thus far and to use this understanding to write out a cohesive, informed interpretation of the Bible.

The following questions may help you gather your thoughts together to "unseal" (remember the meaning of *hermeneutics*?) the meaning of this passage.

- Paul mentions the Christian virtue of "humility" a couple of times in this section (2:3, 8). Why do you think he emphasizes humility in his letter to the Philippians?

ANSWER

- Although Paul is very positive in Philippians, he does bring up the subject of "grumbling" and "arguing" in 2:14. What do you think this tells us about the Philippian congregation?

ANSWER

- The phrase "poured out like a drink offering" is taken from the sacrificial system in the Temple (see Ex. 29:40-41; Num. 29:16-38). Considering what Paul has said in 1:20-23, what might Paul be referring to here?

ANSWER

3   LESSON THREE

Now is the time to gather up all of your insight from this study and write out your interpretation of this extraordinary portion of the Bible.

MY INTERPRETATION

_____

_____

_____

_____

_____

_____

_____

_____

_____

_____

_____

_____

_____

_____

_____

_____

_____

My Interpretation Continued

DEVO†E

In Philippians 2:1-18, Paul is extending a heart-felt pastoral plea to this wonderful congregation in Philippi. Nothing would make him happier in the Lord (2:2) than for the Philippians to undergo a serious "heart checkup." That is, he wants them to be agreeable ("to be like-minded"), to have the same sentiment ("having the same love"), and to be literally of the "same soul" (the word *sumpsuchos* literally means "same soul").

There are some serious spiritual challenges contained in these scriptures! They are of such depth and magnitude that they do not fall into the category of a "quick fix." What Paul is getting at in this passage is the continual transformation of our minds and hearts so that we can be more like Christ. Although his expectations are worthy of a lifetime of commitment and prayer, we need to "start anew" each day in our devotion to such Christian virtues. As you prepare to "own" the words of Paul in Philippians, ask God to help you incorporate the life challenges of this passage.

PAUSE *for* PRAYER

In Philippians 2:1-18, Paul is calling us to take on the mind and heart of Christ. He is calling us to put off the "old man" and to "put on" the new man in Christ (see Col. 3:9-10). The imagery here speaks of taking off old, shabby clothing and putting on the "garments of praise" (Isa. 61:3). Thus Paul's words in Philippians are designed to draw us into (remember the root meaning of *induct*?) a kind of living and thinking that evidences the thoughts and practices of Jesus.

This is no small task. What Paul expects in Philippians is nothing short of the ongoing life of discipleship. What he expects is that we "work out [our] own salvation" (2:12) even as we lay hold of God's enabling power by faith (2:13).

This would be a good time to make use of your journal or spiritual logbook. At this time, you rightly feel that you are in touch with what Paul says in Philippians. And you are! But on down the road a bit, your connection to this passage may begin to fade. The journal will provide you with a personal record to once again pursue God's perfect will.

There are so many individuals, who after achieving great accomplishments in life, still feel empty inside. Even though the world showers them with praise, they are plagued with a sense of meaninglessness. It many cases, these individuals are living "out of selfish ambition or vain deceit" (2:3). Paul clearly states that this is not God's will for His children. On the contrary, our lives should be directed "otherward," that is, toward the service of God and the benefit of our neighbor. This is the joy-filled life that Paul is talking about in Philippians. Why not take a moment to write down some ideas on how you can continually experience this God-given joy in your life? The following comments may help you **Devote** yourself to the ever-increasing joy Paul speaks of in Philippians.

- In a "Me first!" generation that is rapidly becoming a "Me only" mob, godly humility can seem so out of place. Yet Paul advises that true life in the Spirit is one that is lived out humbly before God and neighbor. He may have Micah 6:8 in mind. Here the prophet asks, "He hath shewed thee, O man, what is good; and what doth the Lord require of thee, but to do justly, and to love mercy, and to walk humbly with thy God?" (KJV) Yet in Philippians 2:5-11, Paul has a much closer example for us to copy than the prophets of old; he points to the supreme example of Jesus. In fact he commands that we take on the humble mindset of Christ. The Bible says that pride comes before a fall. By encouraging humility, Paul wants to keep us from falling flat on our faces (Prov. 16:18; 1 Tim. 3:6). How about a "heart checkup" with regard to humility in your life?

- There are so many problems in life that we can't do a single thing about. On the other hand, there are many instances in which we can make a real positive difference. If your first response to difficulties is always to grumble, then your positive sphere of influence will be very small indeed. Rather than "shining like the stars in heaven" (2:15), you can quickly be viewed as a "black cloud." Paul's message in Philippians wants you to shine. Why not devote yourself to becoming a shining witness by resisting the temptation to grumble and complain. You will find that your portion of "joy" will increase day by day.

☩⪥ DISCIPLE

In Philippians, Paul wants us to have a deep, mature joy that transcends the hurts and problems of this world. This great epistle is a spiritual prescription that cures the ills of our heart. And there is even better medicine to come as you study along in Philippians! Yet the Scriptures are never content with us just thinking good thoughts about God. True discipleship involves action, but actions seldom become a reality without thinking clearly and intentionally. So with regard to the remedies that Paul sets forth in 2:1-18 . . .

This week, I commit to:

- Setting aside my own will so that spiritual harmony might exist within the group (2:2). This harmonious group setting might be in the home, at work, or even at play. The context doesn't matter. The important thing is that you deny yourself to bring about a spirit of unity in that particular setting.

- Putting others ahead of myself. In at least one specific instance, I will deliberately promote the interest of others and set aside my own desires (2:4).

- Marking the number of times I have grumbled or complained in the first half of the day. In the second half of the day, I commit to replace each of these negative instances of grumbling with a positive instance of thankfulness, praise, and complementing others. (Note: Your Friday list should look a lot better than your Monday list!)

In Philippians, Paul has a way of really getting into our heads. Discipling others in this regard can be tricky. But God can lead you to people who really need the solace Paul provides in Philippians 2:18. Often when individuals seem "to have it all," they are desperate to find a way out of the spiritual emptiness in their lives. Prayerfully be on the lookout for such individuals this week. Also, grumbling and complaining are often a signs of a much deeper problem in a person's life. For example, negativity can be a sign of depression or bitterness. Yet, unlike mathematics, in real life two negatives never make a positive; things only get worse. God's word in Philippians can literally be a life-saver for people who are caught up in the vicious cycle of grumbling and complaining. In light of your newfound understanding of the Bible, you just may have an opportunity to disciple someone in the life-giving power of Philippians!

LESSON FOUR

Philippians

2:19-30

THE JOY OF HAVING
GOOD MENTORS IN THE CHURCH

LESSON FOUR
Philippians 2:19-30
The Joy of Having Good Mentors in the Church

 ## KEY VERSE

But I think it is necessary to send back to you Epaphroditus, my brother, co-worker and fellow soldier, who is also your messenger, whom you sent to take care of my needs (**Phil. 2:25**).

Introduction

By this point in your study, the main aspects of IBS are becoming second nature to you. This knowledge and skill, together with your understanding of Paul in Philippians, will help you discover the deep truths contained in 2:19-30.

As you have already noted in lessons one and two, Paul is in prison in Rome (see 1:7). He is awaiting trial for preaching the gospel (1:12-14). He is not sure how his trial will end, but in the meantime he is still preaching the gospel. He trusts God and believes he will be released soon (1:20-25).

All of this coincides with what we find at the end of the Book of Acts. Here Luke states, "For two whole years Paul stayed there in his own rented house and welcomed all who came to see him.

He proclaimed the kingdom of God and taught about the Lord Jesus Christ—with all boldness and without hindrance!" (Acts 28:30-31). So, in Philippians, we must not think that Paul was chained to a stone wall in some dark, cold dungeon. Luke clearly says Paul is paying rent on his own hired apartment in the capital of the Empire. Nevertheless, he is chained to two Roman soldiers and is not able to leave the premises. This means Paul is under house arrest. And here is the important part for our understanding of Philippians 2:19-30. With regard to prisoners, the Romans felt obligated to provide only two things: *chains* and *water*. Everything else a person would need to survive in prison must be supplied by family and friends. This is why Paul is so grateful for Christian couriers who are able to keep him supplied, not only with the necessities of life, but also with reports on what is happening in the church. In turn, Paul is able to use these individuals to carry his letters to the various churches while he is in chains.

In this section, Paul introduces us to two such courier/servants in the Lord. They are Timothy (2:19) and Epaphroditus (2:25). They are both noteworthy mentors in the Lord, but they differ in some important ways. For example, Timothy is a trusted servant and very dear to the apostle Paul. On the other hand, Epaphroditus is a servant of the church at Philippi. He has been sent by the Philippians to deliver their care package to Paul in prison. Timothy is healthy and strong, but Epaphroditus is sick and weak. It is in these very differences that the large-heartedness of the apostle Paul really comes to light. He esteems both Timothy and Epaphroditus as being of equal value to him, the church, and in their service to the Lord.

The purpose of this evenhanded praise is to teach the Philippians an important lesson. They need to know that the worth of a child of God is not determined by who they are on the outside, but by who they are on the inside. They need to recognize that the value of God's servants is not assessed by what they can do physically, but by the quality of their dedication spiritually. When they can discern this fundamental aspect of the Kingdom, they will experience the full joy of having good mentors in the church. Paul's Epistle to the Philippians is full of lessons like this. Pray now that God will grant His wisdom and power to learn such lessons.

PAUSE *for* PRAYER

"But he said to me, 'My grace is sufficient for you, for my power is made perfect in weakness.' Therefore I will boast all the more gladly about my weaknesses, so that Christ's power may rest on me" (2 Cor. 12:9). This is a great paradox of the Kingdom of God. That is, God's redemptive power is most effective, not in the context of human strength, but in the context of human weakness. Is this not the core message of the cross? The soul-saving power of God did not happen when Jesus calmed the storm (Mark 4:39), but rather when he said, "My God, my God, why have you forsaken me?" (Matt. 27:46). The place of God's salvation is not to be found in the powers of this world, but in the kind of sacrificial service that sees death as gain (Phil. 1:21). This is a lesson that cannot be learned in books, but can only be learned in life. This is the "end game" of true discipleship.

 # THE TEXT

Philippians 2:19-30

[19] I hope in the Lord Jesus to send Timothy to you soon, that I also may be cheered when I receive news about you. [20] I have no one else like him, who will show genuine concern for your welfare. [21] For everyone looks out for their own interests, not those of Jesus Christ. [22] But you know that Timothy has proved himself, because as a son with his father he has served with me in the work of the gospel.

[23] I hope, therefore, to send him as soon as I see how things go with me. [24] And I am confident in the Lord that I myself will come soon. [25] But I think it is necessary to send back to you Epaphroditus, my brother, co-worker and fellow soldier, who is also your messenger, whom you sent to take care of my needs. [26] For he longs for all of you and is distressed because you heard he was ill. [27] Indeed he was ill,

and almost died. But God had mercy on him, and not on him only but also on me, to spare me sorrow

upon sorrow. ²⁸ Therefore I am all the more eager to send him, so that when you see him again you

may be glad and I may have less anxiety. ²⁹ So then, welcome him in the Lord with great joy, and honor

people like him, ³⁰ because he almost died for the work of Christ. He risked his life to make up for the

help you yourselves could not give me.

DISCOVER

The real "heavy lifting" in IBS comes in the **Discover** step. Here you are to actively read and then reread Philippians 2:19-30. Your goal is to latch onto the critical facts of the passage so you can fold them into your interpretation latter on. The **Discover** step is all about hearing what the Bible says before understanding what the Bible means. If we don't do that, we might jump to conclusions about the Word that are not true. There is no help for us, or for anyone else, in things that are untrue.

As always, sample Helping Questions are provided so that you can carefully extract the facts and content of Philippians 2:19-30. Be prepared to develop your own Helping Questions a bit later. Your own work is what draws you into the world of the Bible. As you grasp the Word, you are grasped by it. In this way, your personal experence with the Bible helps you remember its important lessons. All of this means that a lazy learner knows little about God. So let's get to work and answer some Helping Questions!

Sample Helping Questions

By way of introduction, let it be said that the "Timothy" of 2:19 is the same person addressed in the epistles of 1 and 2 Timothy. The Scriptures tell us that upon his conversion (Acts 16:1), Timothy was discipled by his mother and grandmother (2 Tim. 1:5).

- Why do you think that Timothy was so important for Paul in the ministry? (In answering this question carefully reread Phil 2:19-22. Pull out character traits of Timothy that are found in these verses and write them in the space provided.)

ANSWER

- How might 2:21 connect with what Paul has already said in 1:15 and 17? (In answering this question, refer back to the interpretation you made in the last lesson.)

ANSWER

- What were some of the things Timothy did to "prove himself" (2:22) to Paul? (In answering this question, it is interesting to note that the word for "prove" *is dokimēn*. This word was used at the time of Paul to "prove" the gold and silver content of coins.)

ANSWER

ANSWER CONTINUED

- How certain is Paul of his release from prison, considering what he says in 2:23? (In answering this question, it might help to refer back to your interpretation of 1:20, 27; 2:17 in the previous lesson.)

ANSWER

Now it is your turn to make up some Helping Questions. Make sure you craft the kind of questions that will "draw you into" the text of the Bible by using the Who? What? When? Where? Why? and How? pattern. Craft these questions so that they will address significant spiritual issues of the text like the quality of one's ministry, the degree of one's faithfulness, and the like. Write out your Helping Questions and answers below.

MY HELPING QUESTIONS AND ANSWERS

_____

_____

_____

_____

_____

_____

_____

_____

_____

_____

_____

If you have not included these questions, please dialogue with the following:

As noted above, Epaphroditus was another great mentor in the Lord. The Philippians had just sent Epaphroditus to Paul in prison. He was their emissary whose mission was to bring a care package to Paul while he was imprisoned in Rome.

- What are some of the great mentoring traits of Epaphroditus listed in 2:25?

ANSWER

The Philippians were a relatively trouble-free church, especially when compared with churches like those in Corinth and Galatia. But they did seem to suffer from at least one weakness; they always expected things to go well, and when they didn't, they began to worry (see 1:12). Things have not gone well with the Epaphroditus mission, and it appears that they are disappointed in him and worried about the welfare of the apostle Paul. In light of these concerns . . .

- How does Paul affirm and promote Epaphroditus in 2:25-30?

ANSWER

- How does Paul compare the sacrificial ministry of Epaphroditus with the description of Christ's redemption in 2:5-11?

ANSWER

Although we haven't paid much attention to the structure or shape of Paul's letter to the Philippians, it is said that the person of Epaphroditus occupies the center of the epistle. That is, if you counted from the beginning of the letter to the middle and then started at the end of the letter and counted backward to the middle, you would land on Epaphroditus.

- What do you feel is the significance of Paul placing Epaphroditus at the center of his epistle of joy?

ANSWER

You have worked hard on *dis*-covering the facts and content of Philippians 2:19-30 by way of your Helping Questions and Answers. Now, take a few moments to review all that you have learned about this section of Scripture. Summarize your findings next. This kind of review and summary will fix the facts of the Bible in your mind, and this will prove to be very helpful in giving an accurate interpretation later on.

MY FINDINGS

Discern

After completing the Helping Questions, you are in a much better position to give a solid interpretation of this important portion of Philippians. The **Discern** step will only help you in this regard. Take a few minutes to review the marking system and symbols you have used thus far in your study. Note any patterns, comparisons and contrasts, repetitions and important words that have arisen to this point. Try to grasp the "shape" of Paul's thoughts in 1:1-2:18 and determine how this form of thinking about God and His people carries over to 2:19-30. Be ready to discern some new features contained in 2:19-30. You will need to create some new marks and symbols to track these items. But that's okay, because you will surely encounter these features again, if not in Philippians, then in your continued study of the Bible. So gather up your colored pencils and pens and think creatively about 2:19-30. Before you do, take a moment to ask for the Holy Spirit's guidance in understanding God's Word.

Pause *for*  Prayer

In 1 Thessalonians 5:11, Paul exhorts, "Therefore encourage one another and build each other up, just as in fact you are doing." And in 2 Corinthians 13:10, Paul says, "This is why I write these things when I am absent, that when I come I may not have to be harsh in my use of authority—the authority the Lord gave me for building you up, not for tearing you down." In both instances, the intent of ministry, especially on an interpersonal level, is to "build up" others and not to tear them down. It is interesting to note that the word for *build* is *oikodomē,* from which we derive the word *economy.* This word describes the careful construction of a building or the development of a system that is designed to keep things going in the right direction. This is what Paul does for Timothy and Epaphroditus. He "builds them up" before the Philippian congregation by praising their faithful service and character. Pray as you enter into this **Discern** step of IBS that Paul's example will become part of your "authority" in the church. That is, you will look for every opportunity to say "constructive" comments about those you come in contact with, so that the church will continue to go in the right direction.

The following remarks may help you highlight important aspects of Philippians 2:19-30. As you work through them, be on the lookout for ideas and themes that build upon material you have already studied in Philippians.

- Paul continues to focus on warm, positive personal relationships in this section. You might want to skim through the symbols and markings you have used in previous parts of this study and note those that highlight interpersonal relationships.

- Once again Paul's language in this passage contains a lot of emotional content. He speaks of *hope, comfort, confidence, distress, sorrow, anxiety,* and so on. Link these words with similar thoughts you have already noted in 1:1-2:18. These "matters of the heart" are clearly important to the apostle Paul.

- In 2:19 and 28, Paul uses terms for "cheer" and "glad." He wants to lift the spirits of the Philippians. Use a symbol or marking that conveys cheerfulness or gladness. These ideas will appear frequently in Philippians.

- Philippians is Paul's "Path to Joy" but the apostle is not superficial in his communication with the Philippians. He speaks of "sorrow upon sorrow" (2:27) and "having less anxiety" (2:28). In your marking system, you might want to develop a way of "mapping" the "ups and downs" (↑↓) of Paul's emotional language in Philippians.

- In 2:25, Paul uses a lot of "together words" to describe Epaphroditus, such as "working together" and "soldiering together." Try to develop a symbol that reflects a close partnership in the ministry.

As you work through the **Discern** part of IBS, continue to use symbols that are easy for you to remember. Most importantly, use markings that will clearly communicate an important idea or concept to you. Again in this section, Paul uses terms that refer to positive character traits in a person (↑) and negative traits (↓). You will note also that he uses a lot of "sending" (→) words. Philippi enjoyed a proud military heritage, so Paul employs military images and jargon in this epistle. He speaks of Epaphroditus as a "fellow soldier" in 2:25. So you might want to employ something like a small shield or sword to represent the military aspects that come forth in Philippians.

As you continue to increase your toolbox of markings and symbols, in time you will be able to quickly pick up major themes in the Bible at a glance. That is, if you selected a small dove symbol for the Holy Spirit, then you can skim over an entire book of the Bible and easily see where the Holy Spirit is mentioned throughout that book. Also, by way of your Helping Tools, you will be able to customize your personal devotions in the Bible. For examples in Philippians, if you need to focus on portions that emphasize *joy* and *cheer*, just locate symbols or markings that pertain to this theme. Similarly, if you need to be reminded of the harmful effects of anxiety and worry, just trace out those themes too.

Continue to mark, highlight and insert symbols in Philippians 2:19-30 until you feel that you have identified all significant words and ideas in the passage. Keep in mind what you have already done in 1:1-2:18. Make sure to maintain a degree of continuity here so you can "string together" similar themes as they surface in your study. This work will *un*-cover (recall the Greek word for "truth"?) the special patterns and emphases in Paul and will position you to make a good interpretation of this rich passage in Philippians.

Now is the time to gather up all of the facts that you have observed by way of your Helping Questions and all of the patterns and emphases that you have discerned by way of your Helping Tools. The point here is to use all that you have learned and render a clear interpretation of Philippians 2:19-30.

➡PULLING IT ALL TOGETHER⬅

Here are a couple of final observations that might factor into your interpretation.

- The Philippians had sent Epaphroditus to minister to the apostle Paul. Yet he had fallen ill and Paul had to minister to Epaphroditus! Even before Paul could write the Philippians about what had happened, they had already heard that Epaphroditus was ill. What does this tell you about communication in the early church?

ANSWER

- Before sending Timothy and Epaphroditus to Philippi, Paul highly commends both of these servants to the church. What does this say about the necessity of "letters of recommendation" in the early church?

ANSWER

ANSWER CONTINUED

Your moment of truth has arrived! Study all of your Helping Questions and Helping Tools and write down your interpretation below.

MY INTERPRETATION

MY INTERPRETATION CONTINUED

DEVOTE

All throughout Philippians 2:19-30, Paul describes and celebrates the value of mature mentors in the Church. Timothy and Epaphroditus represent the kind of "fellow workers" and "fellow soldiers" Paul can rely on in ministry. They not only are servants of the church, but they are also Paul's lifeline to the churches. They are devoted to a life of selfless service. Moreover, in the case of Epaphroditus, he was willing to spend himself on the ministry, even unto death (1:27). This is what the **Devote** portion of IBS is all about—the complete surrender to God in service of others. Paul would invite us to experience the life of discipleship that was exemplified by Timothy and Epaphroditus. Let's "Pause for Prayer," praying that the discipling power of the Spirit continue to lead us on this *Path of Joy.*

PAUSE *for* PRAYER

In Ephesians 4:11-13 Paul teaches:

> *So Christ himself gave the apostles, the prophets, the evangelists, the pastors and teachers, to equip his people for works of service, so that the body of Christ may be built up until we all reach unity in the faith and in the knowledge of the Son of God and become mature, attaining to the whole measure of the fullness of Christ.*

In this scripture, Paul points to Christ as the source of gifted people in the church. These precious "gifts" to the church have a clear job description. They are "to equip his people for works of service." The purpose of this "equipping" is "so that the body of Christ may be built up." The word for "built up" is *oikodomēn*. It is from this word that we get our English word *economy*. It refers to the kind of constructive input that is needed to smoothly run a household. Timothy and Epaphroditus are the kinds of "gifts" Christ had given to equip the saints for the smooth running of the household of God. You are a gift to the church as well. Pray now that you may equip the saints for the smooth and harmonious running of the Church of God.

⊕⊃ DISCIPLE

Philippians 2:19-30 tells us that Paul is really suffering. He is in prison, the outcome of his trial is not certain, and there are people in the church who are glad to have him out of the way. But he refuses to let the negatives of life control him spiritually. Rather, he expresses hope, confidence in God, and most importantly, he sees the good in other people. This is the essence of discipleship. In Christ, we are not to let the falleness of this world determine who we are. Rather, we are to "walk in the Spirit" (Rom. 8:4). Through the Spirit, we are to be, "Casting down imaginations, and every high thing that exalteth itself against the knowledge of God, and bringing into captivity every thought to the obedience of Christ" (2 Cor. 10:5 KJV).

The following comments will help you build an action-packed faith this week. That is, they will grant you a simple spiritual framework to live out the counsel of Paul in Philippians 2:19-30.

This week, I commit to . . .

- Expressing hope in God rather than letting the seemingly hopelessness of this world control my life. (Be specific! Name the discouraging part of this world and then lay hold of the encouraging part of God's Word).

- Finding the good in other people and telling others about them. (A good spiritual exercise would be to genuinely compliment at least one person per day and then share that complement with others in the church).

Discipleship must start with us, but it can never end with us. This lesson focuses on the joy of having good mentors in the church. We are to influence each other for good. This is "disciples making disciples." So seek out another brother or sister you can mentor in the great truths contained in Philippians 2:19-30. Lead them in mature, faithful service; the kind of service that was evidenced in Timothy and Epaphroditus. Help them focus on the hope of God rather than the setbacks of life. Show them the spiritual freedom that comes from building up others in the Lord. If we can do this in the Lord, we will truly be on the *Path to Joy.*

LESSON FIVE

Philippians

3:1-11

THE JOY OF HAVING
THE RIGHTEOUSNESS OF CHRIST

LESSON FIVE
Philippians 3:1-11
The Joy of Having the Righteousness of Christ

 ## KEY VERSE

. . . and be found in him, not having a righteousness of my own that comes from the law, but that which is through faith in Christ—the righteousness that comes from God on the basis of faith (Phil 3:9).

Introduction

There is no need to rehearse the basic steps of IBS here. By this point in your study, you are a real "pro" at extracting data, marking important aspects of the text, rendering an interpretation and applying God's Word to your life and others. So let's just continue on into chapter 3 in the usual way.

In 3:1-11, Paul really emphasizes the Christian virtue of joy (3:1). But beginning in 3:2, the apostle takes an abrupt turn in a different direction. His opening words say it all: "Beware of dogs!" (KJV). His change of tone is so dramatic that some scholars feel that starting with 3:2 and continuing to the end of the epistle, we have a fragment from a different Pauline letter. The theory here is that some portion of a more "combative" letter of Paul has been "pasted into" this part of Philippians.

In response, we must acknowledge that all of the ancient handwritten copies we have of Philippians are written exactly as it appears in your Bible today. That is, we do not have any form of Philippians that leaves out 3:2 and the rest of the epistle. So the written evidence before us is that Paul wrote Philippians exactly as it appears in our modern-day Bibles.

However, there is another explanation for Paul's stern words in Philippians 3. He truely loves the Philippians and doesn't want any harm to come their way. And, there was real harm afoot in the church. There was a cluster of hyper-conservative Jews in the church who had made some confession of faith, but they refused to claim Jesus as the sole way of salvation. They appear to be Pharisees (see Acts 15:1-5) and Paul had to fight their influence throughout the churches in Asia Minor (see Gal. 2:11-16). Basically, they argued that salvation is for the Jews *only*, and if one wants to claim a Jewish Messiah, then you must convert to Judaism first. This would mean that all male Gentiles would need to be circumcised and obey all the Law of Moses. These troublemakers were preaching a work-righteousness religion that destroyed the grace of God in Christ (Gal. 1:6-9).

Paul's love for the Philippians led him to make a "preemptive strike" against these agitators before they came to Philippi. Much of chapter 3 is taken up with warning the Philippians about this Jewish herecy.

Arguably, Philippians 3 is the most "theological" portion of the whole book. The essential elements of salvation by grace through faith are brilliantly presented by Paul. As believers, we need to continually take hold of this message and apply it to our lives. Let us pray that the Holy Spirit grant us the grace to always rely on grace.

PAUSE *for*  PRAYER

In Isaiah 6:1-8, the prophet states:

> *In the year that King Uzziah died, I saw the Lord, high and exalted, seated on a throne; and the train of his robe filled the temple. Above him were seraphim, each with six wings: With two wings they covered their faces, with two they covered their feet, and with two they were flying. And they were calling to one another: "Holy, holy, holy is the Lord Almighty; the whole earth is full of his glory." At the sound of their voices the doorposts and thresholds shook and the temple was filled with smoke. "Woe to me!" I cried. "I am ruined! For I am a man of unclean lips, and I live among a people of unclean lips, and my eyes have seen the King, the Lord Almighty." Then one of the seraphim flew to me with a live coal in his hand, which he had taken with tongs from the altar. With it he touched my mouth and said, "See, this has touched your lips; your guilt is taken away and your sin atoned for." Then I heard the voice of the Lord saying, "Whom shall I send? And who will go for us?" And I said, "Here am I. Send me!"*

Those who trust in their own righteousness for salvation have never really seen God. If they ever did, as Isaiah surely did, they would realize how miserable and wretched they are before the Infinite and Holy One. But, by faith, they would also realize that God, in His mercy, has made provision in Christ to cleanse us from all sin and make us fit for service in His kingdom. Paul wants the Philippians to have a holy vision of God in Christ. He wants us to receive this vision as well. Let's pray that the revelation of the righteousness of God in Christ be ever before us as we study this powerful part of the Bible!

THE TEXT

Philippians 3:1-11

[1]Further, my brothers and sisters, rejoice in the Lord! It is no trouble for me to write the same things to

you again, and it is a safeguard for you. [2] Watch out for those dogs, those evildoers, those mutilators of

the flesh. [3] For it is we who are the circumcision, we who serve God by his Spirit, who boast in Christ

Jesus, and who put no confidence in the flesh—[4] though I myself have reasons for such confidence. If

someone else thinks they have reasons to put confidence in the flesh, I have more: [5] circumcised on

the eighth day, of the people of Israel, of the tribe of Benjamin, a Hebrew of Hebrews; in regard to the

law, a Pharisee; [6] as for zeal, persecuting the church; as for righteousness based on the law, faultless.

[7] But whatever were gains to me I now consider loss for the sake of Christ. [8] What is more, I consider

everything a loss because of the surpassing worth of knowing Christ Jesus my Lord, for whose sake I

have lost all things. I consider them garbage, that I may gain Christ [9] and be found in him, not having

a righteousness of my own that comes from the law, but that which is through faith in Christ—the

righteousness that comes from God on the basis of faith. [10] I want to know Christ—yes, to know the

power of his resurrection and participation in his sufferings, becoming like him in his death, [11] and so,

somehow, attaining to the resurrection from the dead.

DISCOVER

Philippians 3:1-11 is packed with theological truth! It contains the beginning and end of what

it takes to be saved. For these reasons, close work with the **Discover** step of IBS is called for here. The

use of carefully crafted Helping Questions will help you *dis*-cover that salvation is by grace alone, not

by works of the law.

So dialogue a bit with the Sample Helping Questions below to get started, knowing all along that you are going to be called upon to make up some of your own.

Sample Helping Questions

- Why would Paul write, in reference to telling them to "rejoice in the Lord," that it is not "grievous" or "troublesome" for him to write these things to them (3:1)? (In answering this question, you may want to refer to your Helping Tools you have been using since the beginning of the study. Trace out and count the number of times you have highlighted the word *joy* in this epistle.)

ANSWER

_____

_____

_____

_____

_____

_____

_____

_____

_____

- Who do you think the "dogs" are in 3:2? (Reread Acts 15:1-5 and Gal. 2:11-16.)

ANSWER

- Why do you think Paul puts "we are the circumcision" and the phrase "who serve God by his Spirit" side by side? (In responding to this question, Rom. 2:29 might help.)

ANSWER

• How do you think Paul's "boasting" (3:4-6) in his Jewish heritage fits here? (In answering this question, note also what Paul says in 2 Cor. 11:20-31.)

ANSWER

Now it is your turn to develop some good Helping Questions. Remember that your questions should be digging out solid doctrine, for Paul's thoughts in Philippians 3 are focused on proper and improper belief and practice. In the end, your questions and answers will lift out the essential truths of what it means not only to be saved in Christ, but also reveal the only condition to stay saved in Christ. So, do some serious work here and make up some good Helping Questions.

MY HELPING QUESTIONS AND ANSWERS

MY HELPING QUESTIONS AND ANSWERS CONTINUED

_____

_____

_____

_____

_____

_____

_____

_____

_____

_____

Here are a few more Helping Questions that "unpack" the doctrine contained in Philippians 3:1-11. If you have not already addressed these in some way, work with them now.

- What do you think the phrase "a Hebrew of Hebrews" might mean to Paul?

ANSWER

_____

_____

_____

_____

- How can Paul say he was "faultless" with regard to righteousness based on the Law (3:6), but at the same time, say that this kind of righteousness is not enough to be saved? Paul's understanding of the Law is notoriously difficult (see Rom. 7:7-25). In grappling with this issue, you might want to read Gal. 2:16; 3:2-16.

ANSWER

- How is the "righteousness that comes from God" superior to "a righteousness of my own that comes from the law" (3:9)?

ANSWER

As you have surely *dis*-covered, there is a lot of heavy doctrine in this section of Philippians. Now is the time to reread all of your Helping Questions and Answers, and to draw all of these theological "facts" together in an organized way. As you review your work, think in an "integrative" way, trying to see how all of these items might fit together as a whole. This exercise will move you in the direction of giving your own interpretation of Philippians 3:1-11 later on.

MY FINDINGS

MY FINDINGS CONTINUED

_____

_____

_____

_____

_____

_____

_____

_____

_____

_____

_____

DISCERN

You have built up quite an assortment of "Helping Tools" in your study of Philippians thus far. You will want to skim back over all of the markings, symbols, and color-coding you have used and carry any relevant items over to your work in Philippians 3:1-11. Even though Paul is highly doctrinal in this section, he is equally colorful in his writing. Indeed, the combination of "dogs," "dung," and "mutilation" can make for some very creative symbol-making for this passage! But the fun here can have a serious effect on your ability to be infused with Paul's thought as he writes the Bible. Again, the Helping Tools clarify the "shape" of Paul's thought and that, in turn, begins to shape the way we think about God and the Bible. Once our mind is "shaped" like Jesus (2:5-11), it is a short step until we begin to act like Jesus. The goal of discipleship is to shape the thoughts and actions of the believer to be more like Christ. It is also the goal for our present study.

After you have revisited the markings you have used thus far, dive into Philippians 3:1-11 and draw all over the page! But first let's prepare our hearts to receive God's Word from this powerful part of His Word.

PAUSE *for* PRAYER

The psalmist prayed, "Open my eyes that I may see wonderful things in your law" (Ps. 119:18). The word *law* here means the whole revelation of God in the Bible, not just the Law of Moses. It includes the Genesis 15:6 statement: "Abram believed the Lord, and he credited it to him as righteousness." This is the golden text Paul uses in Romans 4:3 to teach justification by faith alone, apart from works of the Law. All of this means that the psalmist knows we can read with the "natural" eye but never really perceive the "wonderful things" contained in the Word. Let's pray now that God might open our eyes to the "wonderful things" in Philippians 3:1-11.

Here are some tips that may help you in devising some Helping Tools for this important part of the Bible.

- The word translated "concision" (KJV) and "mutilators" (NIV) in 3:2 literally means "shred to little pieces." In the Greek, it is a play on words with "circumcision." What kind of message do you think Paul is conveying about those who see circumcision as a requirement for salvation?

- Note the number of times Paul uses the word *confidence* in these verses. You may want to develop a symbol for confidence in the right things (+) and then make up an opposing symbol to represent trusting in the wrong things (-).

- Paul is reflecting upon a dramatic change in his life. He is thinking of his Damascus-road experience whereby the risen Lord called him out of Judaism and into the wonderful freedom of grace in Christ (Acts 9:1-20). So there is a lot of "loss"/"gain" language in this section for you to mark as well.

This should be enough to get you started in developing your Helping Tools. Patterns and emphases will begin to emerge that will feed into your interpretation later on.

➡PULLING IT ALL TOGETHER⬅

Now is the point for the "grand integration" of all that you have been able to identify by way of your Helping Questions and Helping Tools. Reexamine everything you have learned—the facts and patterns and emphases—then blend them into one cohesive interpretation.

Here are a couple of items you might want to throw in as well:

The Greek word for "garbage" (NIV) and "dung" (KJV) in 3:8 was used at the time to refer to human and animal waste.

- What kind of message do you feel Paul is sending about his past successes in Judaism compared to the freedom he now has in Christ?

ANSWER

The word for "become like him" in 3:10 is *summorphizō* and means "to be made in the same shape." The core of this word relates to the word *form* used in Phil. 2:5 which says Jesus was "in the form of God."

- What do you feel this says about Paul's understanding of spiritual formation?

ANSWER

ANSWER CONTINUED

Gather together everything you have learned and write out your interpretation below.

MY INTERPRETATION

MY INTERPRETATION CONTINUED

_____

_____

_____

_____

_____

_____

DEVO†E

There is a lot of "movement" in Philippians 3:1-11. That is, Paul is exhorting us to move away from relying on "the flesh" for our salvation and to completely move in the direction of the righteousness of Christ. This kind of spiritual movement is the essence of devotion. On the other hand, the degree to which we look to ourselves for salvation, to that same degree we turn away from God's provision in Christ. Herein lies the main difference between a self-promoting form of religion that leads to death, and a dynamic, personal faith in God that leads to life. Prior to his conversion, Paul had been completely given over to the former and it led him to be a murderous persecutor of the church (3:6). Fortunately, the pure grace of God rescued Paul from himself and gave him Someone infinitely righteous and holy—Jesus. From that point on, the apostle forsook all self-claim and exclusively clung to the cross of Christ in love (3:9). This kind of radical devotion not only embraces the glory of the resurrection, but also welcomes the "fellowship" of Christ's sufferings (3:10). Thus, Philippians 3:1-11 is calling each of us to this kind of devotion to God in Christ. Let's pray that the Holy Spirit will empower us to rely completely on the righteousness of God, and never look to ourselves for salvation.

PAUSE *for* PRAYER

Paul's radical vision of the righteousness of God did not originate with him. As we have already seen, the ancient prophet Isaiah became fully aware of his own sin when he received a glimpse of the holiness of God (Isa. 6:1-8). Later in his prophetic vision, Isaiah proclaims, "All of us have become like one who is unclean, and all our righteous acts are like filthy rags; we all shrivel up like a leaf, and like the wind our sins sweep us away" (Isa. 64:6). "Like the wind our sins sweep us away"—Isaiah's words are beautiful and terrifying at the same time! The question that Paul poses to us in Philippians is, "Sweep us away to where?" May our continual prayer be that the wind of the Spirit forever sweeps us away into the arms of Christ; for it is here alone that we will find the righteousness of God.

The following questions and comments will help you fully receive the valuable lessons contained in Philippians 3:1-11.

- To what extent do I have an "achievement" mind-set when serving God? Have I unreservedly accepted the grace of God, or do I depend on my own accomplishment to merit the good things of God?

ANSWER

- If I have failed God in the past, can I trully "forget those things which are behind" and move forward in the Lord?

ANSWER

- Am I able to see suffering for Christ as a vital part of my discipleship in the Lord?

ANSWER

A prayfully kept journal can be of great help in your study. Have a talk with your heart concerning the spiritual challenges set forth in Philippians 3:1-11. Expressing your thoughts in writing can open up new avenues of devotion to God. Also, revisiting your commitments in the future can motivate you to go deeper in the Lord.

✠⋈ DISCIPLE

Nothing could be more relevant to discipleship than Paul's words in Philippians 3:1-11. Forsaking ourselves in favor of the divine perfection of Jesus is what makes us His disciples. Yet there must be a determined effort on our part to turn from self-righteousness and turn to the righteousness of God in Christ. This "turning" is not an achievement on our part, but rather an acknowledgment that we can't do anything but rely on Christ. This "turning" is not a "work," but rather a surrender to the work of the Holy Spirit so He can make us like Jesus. When this wonderful transformation really happens, that is when we can exclaim with the apostle Paul, "Thanks be unto God for his unspeakable gift!" (2 Cor. 9:15 KJV).

The following points may help you continually receive the pure gift of God's righteousness.

This week, I commit to . . .

- Examining my motives for living a Godly life. Am I acting out of love and gratitude for God, or am I seeking to establish my own basis for acceptance and salvation? Is my success in obedience a matter of divine privilege and Spirit enablement, or has it become a matter of pride and religious achievement?

- Turning away from self and unreservedly turning toward God. My constant aspiration is to be lost in Him so that I can be found in grace.

Some of the most miserable people in the Gospels were the Pharisees. Paul should know because he was a Pharisee (Phil. 3:5). In short, the self-righteous person is an unhappy person. They always think they need to "measure up" and, as might be expected, always sense that they are "falling short." In some cases, this lethal mix of striving and failing can lead to a bitter and vengeful spirit, as it did with Paul before his conversion. An important role of discipleship is, with the help of God, to lead persons out of the pit of self-justification and into the liberty that comes from sole reliance on Christ. As Paul states, "Stand fast therefore in the liberty wherewith Christ hath made us free, and be not entangled again with the yoke of bondage" (Gal. 5:1 KJV). When we can disciple others in the true freedom that comes from the gospel of Christ, then both we and they are on the *Path to Joy*.

A PENTECOSTAL APPROACH to BIBLE STUDY

LESSON SIX

Philippians

3:12-21

THE JOY OF WALKING IN FAITH

L E S S O N   S I X
Philippians 3:12-21
The Joy of Walking in Faith

KEY VERSE

Not that I have already obtained all this, or have already arrived at my goal, but I press on to take hold of that for which Christ Jesus took hold of me. Brothers and sisters, I do not consider myself yet to have taken hold of it. But one thing I do: Forgetting what is behind and straining toward what is ahead, I press on toward the goal to win the prize for which God has called me heavenward in Christ Jesus (Phil. 3:12-14).

Introduction

Our last lesson ended with Paul's powerful statement:

I want to know Christ—yes, to know the power of his resurrection and participation in his sufferings, becoming like him in his death, and so, somehow, attaining to the resurrection from the dead (Phil. 3:10-11).

He ends this present lesson in the same way. Paul teaches:

But our citizenship is in heaven. And we eagerly await a Savior from there, the Lord Jesus Christ, who, by the power that enables him to bring everything under his control, will transform our lowly bodies so that they will be like his glorious body (Phil. 3:20-21).

Our present study is literally wrapped in the resurrection. Indeed, the transforming glory of God embraces everything we will study in this section. Yet, the question remains: "What lies between these two great visions of resurrection glory?"

Paul's answer is clear: Strain forward! Press on! (3:12-13) These two great spiritual challenges, "Strain forward! Press on!" relate well to the great military and sporting heritage of the Greeks. In 490 BC, the Persians stood on the plains of Marathon, Greece, just outside of Athens. Their goal was to destroy Western freedom and impose a cruel dictatorship over all of Europe. They were supremely confident of their mission, for the Persians outnumbered the Greeks by at least two to one. But the Greeks made what appeared to be a suicidal attack. Led by the Athenians, they pressed on, directly into the center of the Persian forces and instilled panic in the enemy. In short order, over 6,000 Persians lay dead on the battlefield with less than 200 slain on the Greek side. A few Persian ships slipped away and planned a direct attack on the city of Athens, but the Greeks were ready for them. A single Greek soldier by the name of Phidippides ran nonstop on a marathon to Athens, a total distance of 26 miles. His goal was to reach the city in time to deliver a two-part message: "Victory in the recent past . . . press on and fight to the finish." He outran the approaching Persian ships, and successfully delivered his message. Freedom from oppression and bondage carried the day.

Yet, having fought on the battlefield earlier that day, the three-hour sprint had left Phidippides exhausted. He died a short time after delivering that momentous message. Nevertheless, his race for freedom had become legendary and birthed the marathon race of the ancient Olympic Games, a sporting tradition that endures to modern times. The proud Greek Philippians would have known this story well. That is why Paul draws upon the inspiring account of the marathon in Philippians 3:12-21. He exhorts the saints to press on to the goal line of freedom in Christ!

PAUSE *for* PRAYER

Paul was a great sports fan. He often used the imagery of athletic competition to teach spiritual lessons. This surely is the case in Philippians 3:12-21. The same holds true for 1 Corinthians 9:25-27. Here Paul states:

> *Everyone who competes in the games goes into strict training. They do it to get a crown that will not last, but we do it to get a crown that will last forever. Therefore I do not run like someone running aimlessly; I do not fight like a boxer beating the air. No, I strike a blow to my body and make it my slave so that after I have preached to others, I myself will not be disqualified for the prize.*

In this instance, Paul accesses the word pictures of running and boxing. The common element that joins both of these sports is determined discipline "to get a crown" (compare 1 Cor. 9:25 and Phil. 3:14).

This is the race of discipleship! It is a joy-filled marathon in the Spirit that ends in glory. Pray now, as you are "drawn into" or "inducted" into Philippians 3:12-21, that God will give you the wisdom and strength to run a good race for freedom in Christ.

 # THE TEXT

Philippians 3:12-21

¹²Not that I have already obtained all this, or have already arrived at my goal, but I press on to take hold of that for which Christ Jesus took hold of me. ¹³ Brothers and sisters, I do not consider myself yet to have taken hold of it. But one thing I do: Forgetting what is behind and straining toward what is ahead,

¹⁴ I press on toward the goal to win the prize for which God has called me heavenward in Christ Jesus.

¹⁵ All of us, then, who are mature should take such a view of things. And if on some point you think differently, that too God will make clear to you. ¹⁶ Only let us live up to what we have already attained.

¹⁷ Join together in following my example, brothers and sisters, and just as you have us as a model, keep your eyes on those who live as we do. ¹⁸ For, as I have often told you before and now tell you again even

with tears, many live as enemies of the cross of Christ. [19] Their destiny is destruction, their god is their

stomach, and their glory is in their shame. Their mind is set on earthly things. [20] But our citizenship is

in heaven. And we eagerly await a Savior from there, the Lord Jesus Christ, [21] who, by the power that

enables him to bring everything under his control, will transform our lowly bodies so that they will

be like his glorious body.

DISCOVER

You have already discovered a powerful aspect of Philippians 3:12-21. Paul employs an "athletic

motif" to spur the Philippians on down the road to mature discipleship in Christ. But there are a lot

more guiding concepts contained in this exciting passage of the Bible. So let's once again employ the

five W's and one H questions to literally *un*-cover (recall the literal meaning of "truth" in Greek) what

the Bible has for us in this section.

But first, intensely read this passage and bring all of your powers of observation to bear upon

the text. Remember, this is an "active" and "vigorous" reading of the Bible that is on the hunt for determining facts and ideas that eventually will form the foundation of your interpretation later on. Once you feel you have a good "grasp" (as in the Greek word *katechō*, "to hold onto firmly"), then dialogue with the Helping Questions listed below.

Sample Helping Questions

- What do you think is the "goal" mentioned in 3:12?

ANSWER

- Why, if Christ has already taken hold of Paul for the goal, does Paul have to strive to take hold of it (3:12)?

ANSWER

- How would you explain this "working together" in light of Paul's claim in 1:6?

ANSWER

_____

_____

_____

_____

_____

_____

_____

_____

As you can see, Paul is weaving an intricate network of ideas in Philippians. God's free gift must be received and cultivated, but it is by grace that we can complete the "race" at all. These Helping Questions have just "primed the pump" of the wellspring of truth contained in Philippians 3:12-21. So develop some of your own Helping Questions below in an effort to bring the critical facts to light in this passage. Don't be afraid to ask bold questions. There may be no definitive answer to your question, but the very asking of the question may grant the Holy Spirit an "opening" to say something new to your heart. This alone will advance your "marathon race" toward God's precious goal in Christ.

MY HELPING QUESTIONS AND ANSWERS

Take a look at some additional Helping Questions. If they address some new aspects of Philippians 3:12-21, then answer them in the space provided below.

- What types of "tensions" do you see in this passage of the Bible? Present state verses future glory? Life on earth verses going to heaven? Dialogue with these ideas below.

ANSWER

- How might personal "sanctification" relate to what Paul says in 3:16?

ANSWER

- Why does Paul bring up the subject of "examples" and "models" in 3:17? (Recall the function of Timothy and Epaphroditus mentioned in 3:19-30).

ANSWER

- Who might the troublemakers be in 3:18-19? (You might want to reread 1:15-18).

ANSWER

- What new "word picture" is presented in 3:20?

Answer

The "facts" of this rich portion of the Bible are starting to add up. It would be good to take some time and glean over what you have *dis*-covered so far. So read over your Helping Questions and answers, and summarize your findings to this point. Make sure you identify Paul's main topic in this section, then include all of the "supporting roles" relating to this main topic. If Paul is talking about our "race course" to heaven, then what are some important aspects of running a good race on our way to the "finish line"?

My Findings

MY FINDINGS CONTINUED

_____

_____

_____

_____

_____

_____

_____

 # DISCERN

Your accumulated knowledge of Philippians, plus what you have already learned about Philippians 3:12-21, have put you in a good position to interpret this great passage. As Paul taught us about the "mind of Christ," you have also learned about the "mind of Paul." That is, you are becoming familiar with the "shape" of how he thinks about God and the Church. Your Helping Tools, as used in the **Discern** part of IBS, deserve some credit here. As you skim from 1:1 to 3:21, noting all the patterns, repetitions, contrasts, and so on, be on the lookout for similar items in your present study. Paul is an integrated thinker and he builds on what he has written before.

Break out your "toolbox" of Helping Tools and permit yourself to be truly "drawn into" God's Word. This will only happen if, as Jesus says, "When he, the Spirit of truth, comes, he will guide you into all the truth" (John 16:13). Prepare your heart in prayer to receive the eternal truth of God in Christ.

PAUSE for PRAYER

In 2 Kings 2:11-14, we read:

> *As they were walking along and talking together, suddenly a chariot of fire and horses of fire appeared and separated the two of them, and Elijah went up to heaven in a whirlwind. Elisha saw this and cried out, "My father! My father! The chariots and horsemen of Israel!" And Elisha saw him no more. Then he took hold of his garment and tore it in two. Elisha then picked up Elijah's cloak that had fallen from him and went back and stood on the bank of the Jordan. He took the cloak that had fallen from Elijah and struck the water with it. "Where now is the Lord, the God of Elijah?" he asked. When he struck the water, it divided to the right and to the left, and he crossed over.*

Elisha was sad when his mentor was taken by God to heaven. But for Elijah . . . he was going home. His citizenship had never been in this world; he was born for heaven.

The same holds true for the apostle Paul. He has turned in his passport for this world and taken up the higher residency with God. Pray now with Paul, that through the Holy Spirit, you can loosen your grip on this world and look homeward to your true citizenship, which is in heaven (Phil. 3:20).

The following are some guidelines that may help in developing your marking system for this lesson.

- Notice the double "already" in 3:12. Paul must balance what God has already done for us in Christ with what he has not already done for us. It would be good to develop some scheme for the whole book that affirms what has already occurred for us in the Lord and then to mark what will happen to us in the future. This also applies to the "behind" and "ahead" language of 3:13.

- The Greek word translated "press on" in 3:12 & 14 is a strong one. It can mean "hunt for" or "chase after."

- The word for "goal" in 3:12 is built upon the same root word as "mature" in 3:15. Think of how these two concepts may relate and make a common symbol for them both.

- There is so much "movement" in this passage: "chase after" (3:12 & 14); "walk one foot after another" (3:16); "to walk about" as on an extended journey (3:17-18). All of these "motion" words have powerful implications for discipleship and spiritual formation. You will want to highlight these aspects and tie them in with similar themes in the rest of the epistle.

- The theme of good mentoring is continued in this section. Note good examples cited in 2:19-30 and 3:17, and bad examples set forth in 1:15-17 and 3:18-19. Develop a marking system for these features.

- The phrase "be followers together of me" (3:17 KJV) is from the word *summimetai* and literally means "copy together" or "mimic with." Develop a symbol to reflect the idea of "copying."

- The formation language in 3:21 is built on the same word used to describe the Transfiguration of Christ in Mark 9:2. The "form" language is also used in Philippians 2:5-11. Highlight these features.

These points just scratch the surface of all that is contained in 3:12-21. So think creatively, but work consistently in your marking system. Integrate what you see here with the threads you have already developed in your work thus far. Paul is weaving a tapestry, and with God's help, you will be able to *discern* the beautiful vision that Paul sets forth in Philippians.

➡PULLING IT ALL TOGETHER⬅

As a good farmer (2 Tim. 2:6; James 5:7), you are now prepared to reap a rich harvest from all of the labor you have sown into Philippians 3:12-21. Intensely study everything you have done with your Helping Questions and your Helping Tools. Make note of the "facts" and the "patterns" that have come to light thus far. Bring all of these "discoveries" and "discernments" together so that you can form a single, integrated interpretation. But first answer the following few questions that will help you draw together all that you have learned:

- Who are the good examples of Christian mentors in 2:19-30 and 3:18-19?

ANSWER

- Who are the bad examples in 1:15-17?

ANSWER

- What types of athletic imagery does Paul use in 3:12-13?

ANSWER

- What types of "formation" and "copying" language does Paul use in 3:17, 20?

ANSWER

- What do you feel is the significance of the "citizenship" language in 3:19?

ANSWER

Gather up all of the inputs of your study thus far and render an informed, integrated interpretation.

MY INTERPRETATION

MY INTERPRETATION CONTINUED

_____

_____

_____

_____

_____

_____

_____

_____

_____

_____

_____

DEVOTE

Paul has placed some formidable spiritual challenges before us, but they are beautiful. We are to turn away from the past and turn to the future in Christ. We are to aggressively pursue after the high calling of Christ. Paul commands us to "walk step-by-step," and to "walk along" like on a long journey. We are to "copy" and "mimic" the sterling example of Paul and his coworkers. We are to loosen our grip on this world and fully register our citizenship in heaven.

If we walk "in the flesh" none of this is possible. But if we "walk in the Spirit" (Rom. 8:1-5), all things are possible with God's help (Matt. 19:26; Mark 10:27).

Take a few moments to bow in prayer. Ask God to help you fully surrender to the empowering expectations of Philippians 3:12-21.

PAUSE for PRAYER

In 2 Corinthians 1:8-9, Paul states:

> *We do not want you to be uninformed, brothers and sisters, about the troubles we experienced in the province of Asia. We were under great pressure, far beyond our ability to endure, so that we despaired of life itself. Indeed, we felt we had received the sentence of death. But this happened that we might not rely on ourselves but on God, who raises the dead.*

Paul is no "Pollyanna." That is, he is not a person who is so superficially positive that he ignores the difficulties and suffering of this life. No . . . he is fully aware of the hard times, but refuses to be defined by them. He has a higher calling; one that is powered by the resurrection and glory. Pray now that you can let go of the setbacks in your life and turn to the life-giving power of the Spirit that leads to what the apostle describes as "an eternal [weight of] glory" (2 Cor. 4:17).

The following questions may help you commit to the scriptural mandates found in 3:12-21. Take a few moments to prayerfully read over them. The guiding question for this part of IBS is: In light of all that I have learned from Philippians 3:12-21, what does God want me to do?

ANSWER

- In 3:12-14, Paul uses an athletic image to describe the quality of his life in Christ. What athletic sport would describe your life in Christ at this moment?

ANSWER

- In 3:17, Paul presents himself as a good Christian model for the Philippians to copy. What do you see in yourself that you would invite others to copy?

ANSWER

- On a scale of 1-10, with 10 being the highest level of investment, to what degree are you a "citizen" of this world? To what degree are you a "citizen" of heaven (3:19)?

ANSWER

- The Lord has certainly transformed your life! List some areas that the Lord has transformed in your life. List some areas that you feel need to be transformed (3:21).

ANSWER

Take out your spiritual journal or log and jot down some notes on how you an "get in shape" for the spiritual contests contained in this passage. That is, view the various areas of discipleship as athletic competitions that you need to train for. Devise some "daily" exercises," like setting specific times for prayer and Bible study. Write in a way that Paul would be pleased to read your journal!

✠⊃< DISCIPLE

As you have no doubt clearly noted, Philippians 3:12-21 could serve as one's personal "Discipleship Manual." It has everything a believer needs to become more like Christ. The past is dealt with, present action is clearly defined, and future destiny is gloriously revealed.

As you enter into this discipleship part of IBS, your journal will serve you well. That is, the course that Paul sets before us in this passage is a marathon race, not a sprint. Yet, even the mighty marathon begins with the first tentative step off the starting block. It is time to see God's "goal line" from where we are right now and start moving in that direction in Christ.

This week, I commit to . . .

- Truly forgetting anything that seeks to slow down my spiritual progress toward the high calling of Christ. Each time a dysfunctional thought rises up from the past, I commit to replacing it with a hopeful, forward-looking promise of God.

- "Hunting" for a new level of spiritual existence in Christ. Regardless of where that may be found, whether in church, in my devotions, or just the random experiences in life, I will be on the "lookout" for an opportunity to climb higher in Jesus.

- Observing someone that I really admire in the Lord and simply copying what he or she does. Be specific here! If they pray, then you pray. If they complement, then you complement, and so on. Find that worthy model and "mimic" it.

- Reassess my hold on this world, especially as it relates to my "citizenship" in heaven. The discipleship goal here is to lay hold of God's perspective on our true identity and destiny in the Lord.

In addition to all of this, you can be a mentor to an aspiring brother or sister in the Lord. Don't sell yourself short! You don't have to be a perfect example to be a good example. In other words, as you become discipled by the Lord, you are well-positioned to disciple others in the Lord. And, as you are "formed" by the Spirit and are used by God to "transform" others in the Spirit, you will make extraordinary progress along your *Path to Joy!*

LESSON SEVEN

Philippians

4:1-9

THE JOY OF GODLY TRUST, PURITY, AND PEACE

LESSON SEVEN
Philippians 4:1-9
The Joy of Godly Trust, Purity, and Peace

 ## KEY VERSE

Do not be anxious about anything, but in every situation, by prayer and petition, with thanksgiving, present your requests to God. And the peace of God, which transcends all understanding, will guard your hearts and your minds in Christ Jesus (Phil. 4:6-7).

Introduction

Each of the lessons in *Philippians: A Path to Joy* has included a section titled "Pulling It All Together." The purpose of this portion of IBS is to summarize the main points of your study. Paul's last chapter to the Philippians could also be titled "Pulling It All Together." This is true because, in his final words to this dear church, Paul summarizes all of the main features of Philippians. For example, his command to "stand firm" (4:1) echoes what he has already said in 1:28. The mention of good mentors and fellow workers in 4:2-3 parallels the examples of Epaphroditus and Timothy in 2:19-30. The quality of a healthy Christian state of mind expands upon the mind of Christ theme in 2:5-11. Finally, his exhortation to "practice" everything they have learned, received and heard from him reemphasizes the command of 3:17. Recall that in 3:17 Paul exhorts the Philippians to "copy" or "mimic" him and his coworkers in 3:17.

This kind of summary in Philippians evidences the superior writing skills of the apostle Paul. From the first word to the last, Paul has thoroughly integrated each thought in this great epistle. If you have been careful in the creation of your Helping Tools, the cohesive nature of Philippians has become clear. In fact, as you prepare to interpret this final chapter of Philippians, you should skim over all of the symbols, markings, and highlighting you have used thus far in your Helping Tools. Notice "concept threads" that run throughout the letter. By following out these common themes in the epistle, you will be able to "see" the pattern of Paul's thought in Philippians. You will see how one thought connects to and then builds upon the next point that Paul makes. This exercise alone will help you "hold together" the various aspects of Philippians.

This brief introduction is enough to show you how important chapter 4 is for Paul's overall purpose in Philippians. In fact, if you do a good job on this lesson, everything that you have learned thus far about Philippians will fall into place. But, before you launch into this summative section of the letter, take a moment to prepare your heart in prayer.

PAUSE *for* PRAYER

When contemplating the joyous virtue of unity, the psalmist exclaims, "How good and pleasant it is when God's people live together in unity!" (Ps. 133:1). The basis for his bold assertion is that spiritual unity lies at the very heart of God. Indeed, the Holy Trinity eternally exists in a state of perfect unity, and it is God's will that His people also dwell in unity. The Philippian church was the most trouble-free congregation that Paul had the honor of founding. Yet, the Philippians were not without their problems. We have already discovered that they were tempted to worry when things did not go as planned. Now, in chapter 4, we see that at least two of their members are at odds with each other. For the sake of the entire church, Paul exhorts these two members to be reconciled one to another. This tells us that even a little bit of disunity can undermine the health of the whole congregation. Pray now that you can be at peace with those about you, and that you can be a peacemaker (Matt. 5:9).

 # THE TEXT

Philippians 4:1-9

[1]Therefore, my brothers and sisters, you whom I love and long for, my joy and crown, stand firm in the Lord in this way, dear friends! [2] I plead with Euodia and I plead with Syntyche to be of the same mind in the Lord. [3] Yes, and I ask you, my true companion, help these women since they have contended at

my side in the cause of the gospel, along with Clement and the rest of my co-workers, whose names

are in the book of life. [4] Rejoice in the Lord always. I will say it again: Rejoice! [5] Let your gentleness

be evident to all. The Lord is near. [6] Do not be anxious about anything, but in every situation, by

prayer and petition, with thanksgiving, present your requests to God. [7] And the peace of God, which

transcends all understanding, will guard your hearts and your minds in Christ Jesus. [8] Finally, brothers

and sisters, whatever is true, whatever is noble, whatever is right, whatever is pure, whatever is lovely,

whatever is admirable—if anything is excellent or praiseworthy—think about such things. [9] Whatever

you have learned or received or heard from me, or seen in me—put it into practice. And the God of

peace will be with you.

ISCOVER

There are many wonderful "facts" waiting to be "pried out" of this final chapter in Philippians. Here you will use your five W's and one H questions to identify and observe important features contained in the text. The items that you *dis–cover* or literally "take the veil away" in this exercise will inform your interpretation of Philippians 4:1-9. As was the case in the other lessons, sample Helping Questions are provided to get you headed in the right direction.

Sample Helping Questions

- What kind of military imagery might be conveyed by the words "stand fast" in 4:1. (It is interesting to note that the standing orders for a centurion in the Roman army was to "stand their ground").

ANSWER

- Why do you think Paul uses such affectionate words in 4:1? (To respond here, skim over your Helping Tools and sift out those that convey strong positive emotions).

ANSWER

- What other parts of Philippians might relate to Paul's phrase "to think the same thing"? Here you will want to trace out parts of Philippians that address the Christian state of mind (see Phil. 2:5-11).

ANSWER

ANSWER CONTINUED

- How do the two women mentioned here live up to their names? (It is interesting to note that *Euodia* means "a good fragrance," and *Syntyche* seems to be derived from the idea of "to meet together").

ANSWER

- How might the theme of good mentors, a theme you have already studied in 2:1ff., relate to what Paul says in 4:3?

ANSWER

Now that you have been "drawn into" or *inducted* into the text of 4:1 by the sample Helping Questions, it is your turn to create some Helping Questions of your own. Read the text carefully and create question from the five W's and one H questions we have been using. Try to devise a question and answer that will bring to light the important facts contained in this section of Philippians.

MY HELPING QUESTIONS AND ANSWERS

MY HELPING QUESTIONS AND ANSWERS CONTINUED

Now that you have observed the text by way of your own Helping Questions, here are a few more that might lead you to *discover* new facts about Philippians 4:1-9.

- Where has Paul previously mentioned "joy" in his letter to the Philippians? (If you have used a particular color for "joy" in your Helping Tools, your answer to this question will be easy. Just skim through your notes and see each place that the color "joy" shows up in your work).

ANSWER

- Why do you think the word "Rejoice" is in the imperative or command mode in 4:4?

ANSWER

The **Discover** step of IBS has enabled you to observe many key facts in 4:1-9. These facts echo themes and images that Paul has previously introduced in his letter to the Philippians. Quickly review all of your Helping Questions and answers and summarize the really important items that you have observed in this section. Write out your findings in the space provided.

MY FINDINGS

 # DISCERN

By now, you have sensed the "pulse" of Paul's heart in Philippians. Your Helping Tools have contributed much in this regard. That is, as you have developed special ways of marking key portions of the text, you have come to notice important emphases of Paul's work in Philippians. Look at some of the key ideas that have surfaced as a result of your highlighting, color coding and underlining of the text. Quickly read over Philippians 4:1-9, and trace out similar themes and images that Paul has used before. Be sure and select the same Helping Tools to highlight these portions of the text being studied. The "shape" of Paul's thoughts in Philippians has become clear by now, and this "shape" of thought continues in this passage. Be on the lookout for new ideas as well, for Paul is a very creative and efficient writer. He will repeat himself (as in the case of "joy"), but he will also add some new ideas. These new elements will expand upon the patterns, comparisons, and contrasts that have been brought to light by your Helping Tools. So, gather up all of your colored pens and creatively discern the truth of God in these verses.

You are getting closer to doing the important task of interpretation. Let's take a moment to focus our thoughts in prayer so that we might better "unseal" (remember the meaning of *hermeneutics*?) the message of God's Word.

PAUSE *for* PRAYER

What goes through our heads is important to God. That is why the psalmist says:

You know when I sit and when I rise; you perceive my thoughts from afar. You discern my going out and my lying down; you are familiar with all my ways. Before a word is on my tongue you, Lord, know it completely (Ps.139:2-4).

With the help of God and His Spirit, we can control what goes through our minds. We can have "the mind of Christ" (1 Cor. 2:16). Pray now that wayward thoughts which do not build up faith, or attitudes which do not reflect the mind of Christ, will be replaced with everything that is good, helpful and hopeful in the Lord.

Here are some comments that will help you discern the wonderful truths of God contained in Philippians 4:1-9.

- The word "contended" in 4:3 reflects military combat.
- Note "the Lord is near" (4:5) picks up on the theme of the Second Coming set forth in 3:20.
- The positive qualities stated in 4:6-8 have been touched on previously in the letter. Note these connections.

There are many more features in this life-changing portion of Scripture. Carry over symbols and marks that apply, but be open to developing new ones.

➡PULLING IT ALL TOGETHER⬅

You have reached the point in your study where you can gather up all that you have *discovered* by way of the Helping Questions and everything you have *discerned* by the use of your Helping Tools. So study through your work and take some notes on the most important parts of your inductive approach to Philippians. Write out what you have learned, keeping in mind that all of this information and literary patterns will feed into your interpretation of Philippians 4:1-9.

Here are a few final thoughts that will give you a solid foundation for interpreting this passage.

- What kind of thoughts and attitudes sap our spiritual strength and contradict the mind of Christ?

ANSWER

- Why are constant worry and the life of faith at odds with one another?

ANSWER

- How might one learn to be inwardly content in spite of one's outward circumstances?

ANSWER

Pray over what you have gleaned from your close reading of the Bible so that you can express an informed interpretation of this passage. Know that what you see in Philippians 4:1-9 will fit nicely with everything that Paul has expressed thus far. Think on the images and topics that Paul has conveyed to this point and carry out the story to the end of this passage.

MY FINDINGS

_____

_____

_____

_____

_____

_____

_____

_____

_____

_____

_____

_____

_____

_____

MY FINDINGS CONTINUED

_____
_____
_____
_____
_____
_____
_____
_____
_____
_____

DEVO✝E

We can certainly empathize with a person who is continually wracked by paralyzing anxiety and worry. Yet, at a very fundamental level, that person does not have a faithful and trusting attitude toward God. They do not believe in the essential goodness of God. They do not trust that He will take care of them, so they worry. Also, Philippians 4:1-9 tells us that bitter and negative thoughts may spring forth from deep hurts in our lives. We may have done absolutely nothing to deserve this pain, but it is there nonetheless. Yet, dwelling on the negative never leads to a way out of our difficulties. It is only when we refuse to indulge the lesser appetites of our souls and minds that we really begin to grow in grace.

This is serious spiritual work. It is the kind of discipleship that can make positive spiritual change, not only in our own lives, but also in the lives of those about us. This kind of change will not come easy, for the devil wants us to be trapped in a vicious cycle of dredging up the negative only to recycle it into more harmful thought patterns that don't help anyone. Yet, there is no time like the present to strike out in a new direction in our walk with God.

This is the time to devote ourselves to the spiritual challenges found in this section. Ask God to show you the way out of old habits of thinking, but don't stop there! Ask Him to lead you in paths of power for His name's sake and for your benefit.

None of this can happen without His help! Pray for God's empowering presence to actualize His Word in your life.

PAUSE *for* PRAYER

In Psalm 19:12-14 the writer says:

> *But who can discern their own errors? Forgive my hidden faults. Keep your servant also from willful sins; may they not rule over me. Then I will be blameless, innocent of great transgression. May these words of my mouth and this meditation of my heart be pleasing in your sight, Lord, my Rock and my Redeemer.*

From these words, we can tell that the psalmist understood the power and the peril of one's inner thought world. He even appears to know something about the subconscious and his limited ability to control that mysterious region of our hearts and minds. But, it is clear that he also knew that God has the power to enter into the deep recesses of our heart and to "clean house."

This is God's will for us. The Bible says, "For God hath not given us the spirit of fear; but of power, and of love, and of a sound mind" (2 Tim. 1:7 KJV). Ask the Holy Spirit to reveal to you the death-bearing thoughts and attitudes of your heart and mind. I say "death-bearing" because things that do not lead to life in God inevitably lead to death. Now, pray for God to do His kingdom work in your heart. Fully welcome Paul's exhortation to the Ephesians when he states, "and to put on the new self, created to be like God in true righteousness and holiness" (Eph. 4:24).

The following comments and questions can guide you along this certain *Path to Joy*:

- Paul calls the Philippians his "joy and crown." This means that they were very precious to Paul. Can you say that your life and faith is someone's "joy and crown"? Pray that in ever-increasing numbers, people treasure your life and witness for the Lord.

- The word for "moderation" in 4:5 can also be translated "yielding" or "gentleness." Paul has already taught that there is a time to stand firm and not to yield (4:1). Yet, there are times when one is to be gentle and yielding. Can you discern the difference here and is this discernment "known to all"?

- Exemplary Christian models are a hallmark of Philippians (see again 2:19-30; 4:9). What qualities in your life would you want others to "copy"? Devote yourself to enhancing these qualities so that others might clearly "learn," "receive," and "hear" your fine witness for the Lord.

This would be a great time to interact with your spiritual journal or log. Often, things written on paper can be "objectified," and so, dealt with more effectively.

✠⊃ DISCIPLE

Philippians 4:9 makes a good transition to the **Disciple** step of IBS. This is true because the root meaning of Paul's word for "learn" in 4:9 is "disciple." So, in Philippians, we have a ready-made model for discipleship. It consists of the kinds of attitudes and habits that we find in 4:4-8.

The kind of change that Paul is encouraging in 4:4-9. will not happen overnight. The renewing of our minds is an ongoing process that continues until we are fully changed by His glorious power (1 Cor. 15:51-52). Yet, on a daily basis, we can determine to take steps in the direction of "glory." That is, with God's help, we can "put on" the new self that has been renewed in the image of the One who created us (Col. 4:10).

The following are some suggestions that can advance your journey along your *Path to Joy*, in light of what Paul has taught in Philippians 4:1-9:

This week, I commit to . . .

- Rejoicing in the Lord, regardless of personal circumstances. By choosing to rejoice in the Lord, I close the door on unwarranted sadness and depression (Phil. 4:4).

- Evidencing gentleness, especially in settings that are full of strife and confrontation (Phil. 4:5).

- Stamping out anxiety and worry. I will replace every anxious thought with prayer and thanksgiving to God (Phil. 4:6).

- Replacing every negative thought with thoughts that are true, noble, right, pure, lovely, admirable, excellent and praiseworthy (Phil. 4:8).

- Living the kind of Spirit-filled life that others can learn from and copy (Phil. 4:9).

Philippians 4:1-9 provides each believer with a wonderful opportunity to disciple others in the Lord. Its positive, uplifting message is good medicine for the world-weary soul. Pray that the Lord lead you to individuals who have lost their joy in the Lord. Share Paul's message of victory with them. You may know of individuals who are consumed with negative thoughts. You can use Philippians 4:8 as a "prescription" to heal their minds and hearts. Indeed, the Lord may use you to disciple those who know what the Lord says, but have tremendous difficulty in putting God's Word into practice (Phil. 4:10). Once they begin to practice Paul's council in Philippians 4:1-9, they will begin to experience the peace of God that surpasses all understanding (Phil. 4:7).

Philippians 4:1-9 imparts the kind of thoughts and habits that bring honor to God. Moreover, as we cultivate the thoughts and practices of Jesus, others will take notice of the grace of God that reigns in our hearts. This is true, because Paul's words in Philippians 4 are not simply words on a page. They are wisdom and they are life. Pray that the Holy Spirit will use this special portion of the Bible to make you an instrument of His peace.

LESSON EIGHT

Philippians

4:10-23

THE JOY OF FREELY GIVING IN THE LORD

LESSON EIGHT
Philippians 4:10-23
The Joy of Freely Giving in the Lord

 ## KEY VERSE

I know what it is to be in need, and I know what it is to have plenty. I have learned the secret of being content in any and every situation, whether well fed or hungry, whether living in plenty or in want (Phil. 4:12).

Introduction

In this final section of Philippians, Paul continues to summarize the main points of his great epistle. In 4:10-23, Paul returns to the love offering that the Philippians had sent to him in prison. Recall that their gifts to Paul were delivered to him by Epaphroditus [see again lesson four, "The Joy of Having Good Mentors in the Church" (Phil. 2:19-30)]. Note again that in 2:25, Paul commends Epaphroditus and describes him as a choice role model for the saints in Philippi. He now mentions Epaphroditus again in 4:18 and is careful to include additional thanks for the gifts that were sent by him. Ever the teacher and mentor, Paul uses the theme of gift giving as an opportunity to further disciple the believers at Philippi. Continuing the theme of rejoicing (see 4:10), Paul now inserts some powerful words about being content in the Lord. He will note that Godly contentment empowers the believer to thrive in all the circumstances of life, regardless of whether one has plenty or if one is in need. Because of God's empowering grace, we can do all things through Christ Jesus who strengthens us (4:13)!

One can already discern that the main theme of Philippians 4:10-23 is the liberating grace of Christian giving. And there is a good reason why Paul emphasizes *giving* at the close of Philippians. He knows that, since the time of the Fall (see Gen. 3:1-19), we are acutely aware of our many needs. We inherently know we are dependent creatures that need to be fed, clothed, and sheltered. We are equally aware that we live in a fallen world of limited resources. All of this means that the universal will to survive tends to make us into "taking" persons and not into "giving" persons. We are born with the sense that things might run out and we might not have enough to make us happy. Indeed, one occasionally comes across a bumper sticker that reads, "I got mine." At a very basic level, we all know what that means.

The problem with being a "taking" person is that we serve a God of unlimited grace. That is, God is a giving Person from first to last. Since the goal of discipleship is to be like God, this means that, if we want to be truly happy, we need to be giving persons too. Let us pray that, with the help of the Holy Spirit, we can set aside that "natural" drive to take and instead seek the gift of the Spirit that grants us the joy of giving in Jesus' name (Rom. 12:8).

PAUSE *for* PRAYER

One of the greatest miracles in the Bible was when God provided for Israel in the wilderness. Throughout the Exodus, God gave the Jews manna from heaven (Ex. 16:11-18). As one reads about this extraordinary gift of the Lord, the words of Exodus 16:18 practically leap off the page. "And when they did mete it with an omer, he that gathered much had nothing over, and he that gathered little had no lack; they gathered every man according to his eating" (KJV). This verse seems to say that the one who hoarded the manna had no surplus, but the one who was not selfish, that is, the one who gathered but a little, had no lack. There is a spiritual paradox here that echoes throughout the Scriptures. The stingy person will experience poverty and the generous person will enjoy plenty. As Jesus said, "Give, and it shall be given unto you; good measure, pressed down, and shaken together, and running over, shall men give into your bosom. For with the same measure that ye mete withal it shall be measured to you again" (Luke 6:38 KJV).

This is what Paul is teaching the Philippians in 4:10-23. Their gift to him by way of Epaphroditus would enrich them far more than it has enriched him.

THE TEXT

Philippians 4:10-23

¹⁰ I rejoiced greatly in the Lord that at last you renewed your concern for me. Indeed, you were concerned, but you had no opportunity to show it. ¹¹ I am not saying this because I am in need, for I have learned to be content whatever the circumstances. ¹² I know what it is to be in need, and I know what it is to have plenty. I have learned the secret of being content in any and every situation, whether well fed or hungry, whether living in plenty or in want. ¹³ I can do all this through him who gives me strength. ¹⁴ Yet it was good of you to share in my troubles. ¹⁵ Moreover, as you Philippians know, in the early days of your acquaintance with the gospel, when I set out from Macedonia, not one church shared with me in the matter of giving and receiving, except you only; ¹⁶ for even when I was in Thessalonica,

you sent me aid more than once when I was in need. [17] Not that I desire your gifts; what I desire is that

more be credited to your account. [18] I have received full payment and have more than enough. I am

amply supplied, now that I have received from Epaphroditus the gifts you sent. They are a fragrant

offering, an acceptable sacrifice, pleasing to God. [19] And my God will meet all your needs according

to the riches of his glory in Christ Jesus. [20] To our God and Father be glory for ever and ever. Amen. [21]

Greet all God's people in Christ Jesus. The brothers and sisters who are with me send greetings. [22] All

God's people here send you greetings, especially those who belong to Caesar's household. [23] The grace

of the Lord Jesus Christ be with your spirit. Amen.

DISCOVER

By this point, you are so acquainted with the **Discover** step of IBS that you could teach others

this important tool for Bible study! First, you need to carefully read Philippians 4:10-23. Diligently search out all the facts contained in this wonderful portion of scripture. As you read, you will want to make mental connections with all that you have learned about Philippians thus far. The "Who? What? When? Where? Why? and How?" Helping Questions will enable you to discover the essential data contained in this section. Don't worry about the meaning of the text at this point; just bring all of your powers of observation to bear on 4:10-23. In this way you will gather enough "raw material" to build a good foundation for continued study later. Be patient and resist the temptation to "jump ahead" in your analysis of this last portion of Philippians. A careful, steady approach to the Word will pay big dividends when it comes time for your interpretation. The following Helping Questions will lead you in the right direction here.

Sample Helping Questions

- What recurrent theme in Philippians do you see at the beginning of 4:10?

ANSWER

- Why doesn't Paul simply say, "Thank you!" to the Philippians?

ANSWER

- How does Paul use the occasion of their gift to teach about godly contentment (see 4:11, 12)?

ANSWER

- How does Paul complement the Philippians in 4:15, 16?

ANSWER

_____

_____

_____

_____

_____

_____

_____

Your careful reading for facts, as well as your responses to the Sample Helping Questions, has "inducted" or "drawn" you into the mind of Paul in 4:10-23. Continue to explore this portion of the Bible by creating some of your own Helping Questions. The very crafting of the questions will cause you to purposefully engage God's Word. This is an important step in the learning process.

MY HELPING QUESTIONS AND ANSWERS

_____

_____

MY HELPING QUESTIONS AND ANSWERS CONTINUED

_____
_____
_____
_____
_____
_____
_____
_____
_____
_____
_____

Your diligent application of the **Discover** step of IBS has taught you much about Philippians 4:10-23. In case you haven't thought of the following Helping Questions, give them a try now.

- Where else in Philippians has Paul mentioned Epaphroditus?

ANSWER

_____
_____
_____
_____

- What special Jewish setting might Paul be referring to when he says, "They are a fragrant offering, an acceptable sacrifice, pleasing to God" (Phil. 4:18)?

ANSWER

- Who might Paul be referring to when he speaks of "Caesar's household" in 4:22? (In answering this question, refer to all that you have already discovered from studying 1:13).

ANSWER

Now is the time to reread all of your Helping Questions and answers. Sift out all of the facts you have discovered from this important step of IBS. Summarize your findings in the space provided.

MY FINDINGS

DISCERN

Paul has set forth this epistle in a very programmatic way. As noted already, the closing of the epistle mirrors the opening of the epistle. Also, the selfless service of Epaphroditus occupies the central point of the letter. Finally, the themes of joy, the humility of Christ, and positive Christian thinking join everything together. You have, no doubt, developed Helping Tools to identify and track these themes and patterns contained in Philippians. Now is the time to review all of the underlining, highlighting, and special symbols you have employed in your study thus far and carry them over to Philippians 4:10-23. So gather your colored pens, and highlighters, and identify key features contained in this section.

But, before you thoroughly analyze this closing section of Philippians, take a moment to ask for God's guidance. You are on the verge of connecting all of the major points contained in Philippians 4:10-23. Moreover, you have been mentally joining together the great truths of Philippians as you have worked along. It is importance to seek the Holy Spirit's leading at this point.

PAUSE *for* PRAYER

In 2 Corinthians 8:1-9, Paul compares the generosity of the Macedonians (recall that the Philippian church was located in Macedonia, Greece) with the reluctance of the Corinthians to follow through on their pledge to give. Paul then writes to the Corinthians, "For you know the grace of our Lord Jesus Christ, that though he was rich, yet for your sake he became poor, so that you through his poverty might become rich" (2 Cor. 8:9). So, Jesus is the ultimate example of Christian giving. He represents that extravagance of grace that is totally given over to the welfare of others. Pray now that in some measure, the unrelenting benevolence of the Lord might become part of your daily conversation with God.

Here are some tips that may assist you in developing good Helping Tools for Philippians 4:10-23. They will lead you to themes and ideas that deserve to be marked and highlighted in some way. Be aware that you have probably marked these items in the previous sections of this study. Carry these markings over to this section as well.

- Paul practices what he preaches. He has strongly exhorted the Philippians to "Rejoice in the Lord!" (see 3:1; 4:1, 4). He opens 4:10 by personally rejoicing in the Lord.

- In 4:10, Paul addresses the subject of Christian giving and receiving.

- In 4:11-13, Paul again speaks to an internal quality of mind. Here he expounds upon the idea of "contentment."

- In 4:19, Paul touches on the principle of "reciprocity." That is, if we sincerely serve others in Christ, God will take care of us.

There are more themes and points contained in this closing section of Philippians. Glean through your Helping Tools and thoroughly apply them to this passage.

➡PULLING IT ALL TOGETHER⬅

Skim through all of the Helping Tools you have used in this section. The point here is to integrate what you have discerned by way of highlighting and symbol-making. You will want to make connections to what you have learned thus far and feed all of this into your interpretation of this last section of Philippians.

The following questions will help you "pull it all together":

- Where else in Philippians has Paul written about giving?

Answer

- How might the theme of sacrificial giving relate to Epaphroditus (compare Phil. 2:25-30 and 4:18)? Write out your thoughts in the following space.

Answer

- Find those portions of Philippians that speak of sacrificial giving and connect these portions with 4:10.

ANSWER

- Search through your work to this point and retrieve the markings and symbols that reflect the idea of completely trusting in the Lord. Write out these scriptures and describe how they relate to what Paul says in Phil. 4:12-13.

ANSWER

ANSWER CONTINUED

_____
_____
_____
_____
_____
_____
_____
_____
_____

- Where else in Philippians has Paul evidenced the concept of divine reciprocity (that is, giving and then receiving)? Reread 2:6-11 and express your thoughts below.

ANSWER

_____
_____
_____
_____
_____

Now that you have drawn together all that you have discerned by way of your Helping Tools, you are well on your way to "unsealing" (do you still remember the meaning of *hermeneutics*?) the meaning of Philippians 4:10-23. To get the most out of your work, combine the patterns, repetitions, and emphases that were brought to light by your Helping Tools with all that you discovered through the application of your Helping Questions. Once you feel you have a good grasp of all of your findings, ask yourself the all-important question, "What is God saying in this passage?" Your answer to this question is your interpretation. Write out your interpretation below.

MY INTERPRETATION

_____

_____

_____

_____

_____

_____

_____

_____

_____

_____

DEVOTE

As you have learned by now, it is not enough to simply know what the Bible means. The real spiritual power starts with asking the question, "What does this passage mean to me?" In other words, What are the spiritual mandates contained in Philippians 4:10-23, and how do they relate to my personal life?" Another way of getting in touch with the practical call of God is to ask yourself the question, "If the apostle Paul was sitting in front of me right now, what would he expect me to do in light of what he has written in this section?"

It is at this point in the study that your spiritual journal or log book can come in handy. As you encounter and respond to the expectations of Paul in this powerful part of the Bible, you might want to jot down some of your reflections on this lesson. Putting your thoughts into words and writing them down on paper will help you get in touch with the dynamic nature of God's Word (Heb. 4:12). Also, when you express your understanding of the Bible, it will impress its meaning and power upon you. Once that happens, you are one step closer to actualizing the claims of the Scriptures in your life.

If the **Discover** and **Discern** steps of IBS focus on enlightenment, the **Devote** step is all about empowerment. Life in the Kingdom cannot be done in the flesh, but it can only be done in the Spirit. The lofty goals of Paul in Philippians 4:10-23 certainly are a call to prayer.

PAUSE for PRAYER

In Acts 20:35, Luke records Paul's words to the Ephesian elders: "In everything I did, I showed you that by this kind of hard work we must help the weak, remembering the words the Lord Jesus himself said: 'It is more blessed to give than to receive.' " What is peculiar about this verse is that the Gospels do not record these exact words of Jesus. Paul may have picked up on a saying of Jesus that was not included in our four Gospels. In any case, his meaning is clear: giving is a more blessed experience than receiving. Again, this is contrary to the mind of the flesh (Rom. 8:5; Eph. 2:3). The natural man (1 Cor. 2:14) thinks taking is better than giving. But, because we are created in the image of God (Gen. 1:26), the exact opposite is true. We are most like God when we give freely. So, we are most blessed when we give and not receive.

The following comments and questions are designed to help you make practical commitments to the lessons you have learned in Philippians 4:10-23. Prayerfully read through these remarks and seek God's guidance in actualizing Paul's teachings in your life.

- On a scale of 1-10, with "10" being the highest degree of generosity, am I a giving person or a taking person?

- How would you gauge your level of "contentment" right now?

- To what extent do you allow your circumstances in life to determine your attitude?

- Do you truly see *giving* as an act of worship?

The Holy Spirit speaks through God's Word. He is able to customize the Bible to address our personal lives in Christ. No doubt, the Lord has spoken many things to you in addition to the questions listed above. Since this is the summary chapter of Philippians, ask the Holy Spirit to do a "holistic" work in your life. That is, invite the Lord to transform and mold you into the pattern that Paul has set forth in the entire Epistle to the Philippians.

This would be a perfect time to skim over all of the notes and reflections you have recorded in your spiritual journal or logbook. In light of what you have recorded their, ask God to help you make summary commitments to the great teachings of Philippians. Affirming and experiencing the joy of the Lord . . . trusting that God is in control . . . cultivating positive, God-honoring thoughts . . . sacrificial giving . . . all of these powerful tools for spiritual growth are part of Paul's message to us in Philippians.

✠ DISCIPLE

There is no greater joy than actualizing the Bible in our lives. Indeed, our entire reason for being is to make God's Word come alive in a free and easy way in our day-to-day walk with the Lord. Below are some guidelines to help the spiritual mandates of Philippians 4:10-23 become real in our lives.

This week, I commit to . . .

- Enhance the joy of another by supplying a definite need in their life. You might consider buying a gift card from a grocery store or restaurant to help someone struggling to put food on their table. Or, you may know of someone who would like to visit a loved but can't afford to go. You might want to purchase a fuel card for them so that they can make this trip. Simply commit to being on the lookout for someone in need and decide to meet that need.

- Looking unto God for my contentment. That is, every time I become dissatisfied with my situation in life, I commit to redirect my thoughts toward the Lord. That is, the foundation for my contentment will be the Lord and not my situation in life.

- Seeing giving as an act of worship. Every time I give, I commit to visualize my gift as devotional incense rising up from the altar of God. My gifts are an acceptable sacrifice that is pleasing unto God (Phil. 4:18).

Being discipled in accordance to Philippians 4:10-23 will be a wonderful spiritual experience! Becoming more like God means being transformed from a "taking person" into a "giving person." It means having an unchangeable and inexhaustible foundation for my contentment. It means that participating in the stewardship of the church will no longer be a matter of obligation but an expression of my worship and devotion to God.

Perhaps the greatest blessing of this lesson is to give it away. That is, pray for the opportunity to disciple others in Paul's teaching on giving. Pray that God will lead you to someone who has never discovered that true contentment comes from the Lord. Pray that the Lord will lead you to someone who is tired of the diminishing returns of taking all the time. In short, pray that God will use you to disciple another in the joy of Christian giving.

A PENTECOSTAL APPROACH
to
BIBLE STUDY

CONCLUDING
REMARKS

Philippians

Concluding Remarks

Paul's Epistle to the Philippians is the good news lived out in the here and now. It is the life-giving atmosphere of the kingdom of God on earth. In this brief letter, Paul builds a network of powerful words and phrases that tear down the strongholds of the devil (Col. 2:15) and send fear throughout the corridors of hell (2 Cor. 10:5). The joy of the Lord . . . the peace of God . . . supreme trust in Jesus . . . all of these are the promised reality for those who are in Christ Jesus!

The resounding message of Philippians is this: It is not God's will for you to live in fear and defeat. Indeed, the Apostle Paul would stand shoulder to shoulder with the ancient prophet Nehemiah and proclaim, " The joy of the Lord is your strength!" (Neh. 8:10).

This is the purpose of this last lesson of *Philippians: A Path to Joy*. By drawing together all that you have learned and experienced in studying this great letter of Paul, you can incorporate more of the joy of the Lord in your life. The mind of Christ will inform your every thought. The sovereign will of God will direct your every action.

Ideally, if you are part of a small group, your group leader will create a context in which you can share all that you have gained from this inductive study of Philippians. Review all of the interpretations you have rendered for each section of Philippians. You may want to recall some of the commitments you made to the Word and the degree that you have followed up on these commitments. Read back through your journal or spiritual log and collect some summary thoughts. All of these review activities will "induct" or "draw you into" the overcoming life that God has for you in Christ.

The following lists will help you recollect the main themes of Philippians as well as some of the spiritual challenges set forth in the Bible. As you prayerfully read through these items, continually ask that the Holy Spirit realize the truth of Philippians in your mind and heart. Pray also that all that has been birthed in your heart by the Holy Spirit become a real part of how you live your life before God and neighbor. This is the heart of discipleship that will continually lead you on God's *path to joy*.

Major themes encountered in Philippians include:

- The joy of the Lord
- God is in control.
- Loving fellowship in the church
- Complete trust in God
- Courage to witness
- The mind of Christ
- Model Christian ministers
- Forgetting what is behind and striving forward to the high calling of God in Christ Jesus
- Our citizenship is in heaven.
- Freedom from anxiety and worry

- Positive thoughts that reflect the mind of Christ

- The joy of Christian giving

- God will bless those who freely give.

Spiritual challenges set forth in Philippians include:

- Continually expressing thanks in prayer

- Forsaking dependence upon worldly things for joy

- Committing to unconditional trust in God and his provision

- Welcoming suffering as a vital means for discipleship in my life

- Denying my own will for the sake of the unity of the community

- Replacing grumbling with a continual offering of thanksgiving and praise to God

- Looking for the good in the lives of other people and sharing this with others

- Examining my motives for serving God

- Seeking out good mentors and models in Christ and "copying" them in the Lord

- Reclaiming my citizenship in heaven

- Forsaking anxiety and worry and replacing these negative aspects with prayer and thanksgiving

- Rejecting every negative thought and replacing it with thoughts and virtues that are worthy of the Lord

- Committing to be a better example of Christ

- Giving unto the Lord as an aspect of worship

The words of Paul to the Philippians are certainly an inspiration to us all. They challenge us to "put off" the negativism and grumbling of the old man and to "put on" the positive, faith-filled life of those who truly know God in Christ. Or, as he states in Ephesians 4:22-25, "You were taught, with regard to your former way of life, to put off your old self, which is being corrupted by its deceitful desires; to be made new in the attitude of your minds; and to put on the new self, created to be like God in true righteousness and holiness." The good news is that this joy-filled life of discipleship is not a product of our own strength, but rather, it is the gift of God. Paul teaches the same thing in Philippians 2:13, which says, "For it is God which worketh in you both to will and to do of his good pleasure" (Phil. 2:13 KJV). Let us allow God to work in our lives through the power of the Holy Spirit. It is His will that we should always make progress on His *path to joy*!

About the Author

William A. Simmons, professor of New Testament Studies and Greek at Lee University, Cleveland, Tennessee, received his Ph.D. from the University of St. Andrews in Scotland. Bill's specialty is New Testament exegesis with a concentration in the Pauline Epistles and Koine Greek. His published works include *Peoples of the New Testament World: An Illustrated Guide; A Concise Background of the New Testament; Paul and Jesus: A Theology of Inclusion; New Testament Survey;* and a commentary on Galatians. Bill has also published several articles in the *Evangelical Dictionary of New Testament Theology* and the Lexham Project for Logos Bible Software. He has also done teaching and mission work at the European Bible Seminary in Rudersburg, Germany, and taught in other countries such as Korea, Honduras, the Philippines, Guatemala, Scotland, Cuba, and Peru. His hobbies include outdoor sports and woodworking. Bill resides in Cleveland, Tennessee, with his wife, Lenae, and has three children: David, Nathaniel, and Laura.